Today's British Army in Colour

A modern British paratrooper.

Below: A 155mm Field Howitzer in towing configuration.

Today's British Army in Colour

JEREMY FLACK

BCA
LONDON NEW YORK SYDNEY TORONTO

This edition published 1992 by BCA by arrangement with Arms and Armour Press, a Cassell Company

CN 5302

Designed and edited by DAG Publications Ltd. Designed by David Gibbons; edited by Michael Boxall; layout by Anthony A. Evans; typeset by Wyvern Typesetting, Bristol; Printed and bound in Great Britain by Bath Colourbooks.

Left: After many years of indecision the Challenger II Main Battle Tank (MBT) has at last been selected for the Army. Following lengthy trials and in competition with the American M1A2, the German Leopard II and the French AMX-40 Leclerc, and evaluation of its performance in the Gulf, the Ministry of Defence has placed an initial order for 127 of the Challenger II to replace the Chieftains.

Right: The AS90 self-propelled howitzer, 179 of which have been ordered at a cost of £300 million, is to replace the Abbot and M109 and is currently in production by Vickers Shipbuilding & Engineering Ltd.

Contents

Above: Shorts produced Starburst as a Javelin development and its existence was only announced following the Gulf War, more than a year after entry into service use. Starburst uses a laser facility for its command to line-of-sight guidance, making it immune to all known countermeasures.

Below left and right: The Army has insisted that it requires a new battlefield attack helicopter for several years. As time has passed the direction would appear to be the US-designed AH-64, Apache, possibly built by Westlands. The success of the Apache, a dedicated tank-killer, was very evident on the Gulf War TV News where enemy tanks were being knocked out as though part of a computer game. **(Right:)** The two-man crew have the IHADSS (Integrated Helmet And Display Sighting System) on which key flight data such as airspeed, radar altitude, and heading can be superimposed.

Introduction

In 1989 I was commissioned by Arms & Armour Press to produce a book portraying the British Army at work as a follow-on to a previous successful book about the RAF. Having been primarily an aviation photographer, but with a keen interest in Army matters, I was aware that the Army was in the process of receiving a variety of new equipment and thought that it would be merely an interesting project, little realizing how much of an under-estimate that would turn out to be.

The purpose of this book is to illustrate the wide range of equipment currently used by the Army in its various locations throughout the world.

When I began work on this project the British Army had been geared up for the long-established 'sit and wait' confrontation of the Cold War. A large proportion of its manpower and equipment was tied up in Germany where, together with the NATO Allies, it was located to deter the overwhelming might of the Soviet and Warsaw Pact countries from any thoughts of an invasion of Europe. The Regular soldiers based in the UK were in the main to provide a reserve for those in Germany. A substantial force of part-time Territorials and Reservists provided a further back-up for the UK and Germany, thus providing the British contribution to the protection of Europe.

Overseas we had a number of commitments. Fortress Falklands had been established and now the manpower levels could be reduced. Gibraltar continued to be a thorn in the side of Spain, but provided a vital eye for Nato on the comings and goings in the Mediterranean.

Involvement in Northern Ireland, where terrorists were committing atrocities under the thinly disguised excuse of political change, meant that the Army was constantly 'on the front line'.

Encouraged by the then Director of Public Relations for the Army, Brigadier Christopher Wallace, I was provided with a broad range of facilities and access to many locations and units that would take me to the extreme outposts of British Army presence throughout the world, from Belize to Hong Kong, and the Falklands to Germany. I regret only that because of timings and commitments I was unable to visit Norway.

The facilities were to be wide-ranging, from joining national pressmen to witness staged battle scenes to spending time with various units during training and exercises. While on the whole all have been extremely interesting, I enjoyed most my visits to individual units, getting to know the officers and men, their reasons for joining the Army and what job satisfaction they get at the end of the day.

The first BAOR winter exercise I encountered was the traditional event formulated around the perceived threat of an attack from the Soviets. BAOR Forces would be mobilized to counter the simulated enemy or 'Orange' forces, being deployed to hold them until reinforcements arrived. At the same time large numbers of Regular and TA soldiers would be deployed from the UK to provide a back-up for the BAOR force already in place and then would start the big push to get 'Orange' forces back behind their border. These exercises were normally NATO organized and involved troops from most of the member countries.

These exercises covered several hundred square miles of West Germany. For some civilians driving through the area the scenes were reminiscent of actual warfare although without the destruction. The 'battles' would flow through forests, fields and towns. Damage and obstructions would be avoided as far as possible, though some were inevitable. Most of the damage would be to farmers' fields by tracked vehicles, so the most intensive exercises would be held during the autumn and winter before the new crops were sown. Compensation if appropriate would be paid by the West German Government.

These exercises have been a fact of life for the West German population since the Second World War and were initially resented as being carried out by an army of occupation. Later, given the East/West confrontation, they were appreciated, especially by those living close to the border with East Germany. The older generations, having experienced the horrors of war, do not want to go through it again and regard the inconvenience as insurance. In recent years younger generations have become more vociferous against the exercises.

With the collapse of the Soviet Union, the ideal world looked as though at last it was in sight. However, such great change has led to a period of instability while the peoples of the world adjust to the new, more open attitudes. Years of distrust and secrecy will not disappear overnight.

While nobody in his right mind wants war – not even the military – man being man gets ambitions and becomes jealous, and in a political leader this becomes highly dangerous. Iraq was the emerging tinderbox. Having failed to achieve anything during a lengthy war with Iran that was punishing for both sides, Saddam Hussein turned his attentions to his small but rich neighbour, Kuwait. In no time at all, the world was in turmoil. Following the failure of negotiations a huge Coalition force was assembled from nations who united throughout the world. When Iraq continued to ignore all United Nations demands to remove his occupying forces the time for diplomacy ran out. Iraq was forced to pull back and the national boundaries were restored at great cost in terms of Iraqi lives.

Opposite page: The GEC Phoenix (to replace Midge) has been designed to provide the Army with the most modern real-time surveillance and target acquisition capability on a day or night basis and in all weather conditions. It can provide the ground crew with live imagery of enemy positions up to 50 kilometres behind their lines, enabling effective control of artillery fire, vital for MLRS.

Above: Thorn EMI ASTOR (Airborne STand-Off Radar) has been fitted to a Pilatus Britten-Norman Islander as a technology demonstrator in order to assess the effectiveness of stand-off radars in 'over the border' and battlefield surveillance roles.

Right: Shorts have been working on the replacement for the Javelin missile. This is to be called Starstreak and is unique in that it consists of a pair of motors and three darts. Having been accelerated to many times the speed of sound, the three darts separate and are guided to the target by the aimer. Starstreak has been ordered with multiple launchers mounted on the Stormer APC.

This period of turmoil has been the very one during which I have been compiling this book. It has been a tremendous era in world history. So many of the established positions of power and entrenched ideologies have changed that there is greater hope now for world peace, but great care must still be taken in order to achieve it. As with the defence cuts announced in the early 1980s which were rapidly followed by the Argentinians invading the Falklands, the current reduction in forces has been served with a forceful reminder that the ideal is not easily attained and certainly cannot be achieved overnight.

Post-Gulf, the announced Options for Change talk of reductions of Army strength by 40,000 men to 116,000, these to be implemented over a four-year period. There is no doubt that these cuts will see yet another painful period in the history of the British Army. While the Army will survive, I hope that when completed these changes will enable the politicians to see their way forward positively.

During the last few years a large number of good men and officers have left the services, demoralized and disillusioned. I have seen regiments that have sunk below strength, to an unworkable degree in some cases. Insufficient equipment has affected training. While manpower accounts for a substantial proportion of the defence budget, a reduction in levels will not produce a massive saving. With the falling apart of the Warsaw Pact – even talk of some of the countries wanting to join NATO – and the break-up of the Soviet States, the new openness may produce a level of peace that has not existed in living memory. Some of the weapons that have been deployed to maintain this peace will become surplus to future requirements, but other more appropriate equipment will be needed and funding will still be required.

The Army of the future will most likely be highly mobile with a really effective capability. It will be able to move quickly to any potential trouble-spot and act as a deterrent. It is interesting to see the announcement that 24 Airmobile Brigade is being combined with the Paras, Royal Marines and ACE Mobile Force, all of whom are quick-reaction forces, to form a new Strategic Reserve Division within the Options for Change. NATO is also talking about a Rapid Reaction Force of which this may be part.

The military is like an insurance policy. One hopes that one will never require it, but one has to pay the premiums just in case. One can shop around and save money on a cheap policy, but if one has to make a claim it may be found ineffective. The role of the British Services is one of deterrence. For this to be credible it must appear to be an effective force. Simply to destroy our military power will not necessarily lead others to do the same. We have already tried it with chemical weapons, thirty years ago, and were threatened with attack by these weapons by Iraq during the Gulf War; the Iraqis had already used them on previous occasions.

The Army is receiving substantial quantities of new equipment to replace obsolete and inefficient items. Some of these, such as MLRS, have already proved their worth during the Gulf conflict and are revolutionizing military tactics. However, these items of equipment take many years to evolve and it is important that the design and development of new equipment continue to take place.

A variety of new pieces of equipment are due to enter service shortly or are about to be ordered. These range from the Challenger II to the AS90 Self-Propelled Howitzer and Phoenix remote-controlled surveillance craft, which are now in production, and the eagerly awaited new anti-tank helicopter, likely to be the Apache.

While it would be a fine ideal to be able to dispense with the military, they will always be needed to protect us and our way of life. It may be difficult to decide whether we should have a new school, hospital or regiment of tanks, but without adequate protection we might end up with nothing. While the world is talking about peace the Serbs and the Croats are killing one another. Where is the next tinder-box waiting to engulf us?

The following pages chart my attempt to keep abreast with this amazing period through which we are living. Illustrated are the soldiers in Northern Ireland who risk their lives on a daily

Above: Alvis have designed a new family of Armoured Fighting Vehicle (AFV) to replace the existing Scorpion family. While a number of the family are still at the design stage, others have been in development for some time, some seeing service in the Gulf.

Below: The BAe Merlin is designed as an intelligent anti-armour mortar weapon. Fired from a standard 81mm launcher, on reaching the top of its trajectory the seeker head is switched on and its priority is to look for moving targets such as MBTs and APCs in an area of approximately 300×300 metres, failing which it will then search for stationary targets.

basis; patrols in foreign countries to help weaker nations maintain their freedom while under possible threat from a stronger neighbour, and thus preserve their way of life; EOD teams who daily risk their lives to make safe weapons of previous wars or those planted by terrorists and found in our towns and cities; and the soldiers who went to the Gulf expecting a horrendous cocktail of chemical and biological weapons.

I have found this a fascinating world and am grateful to all those involved for the invitation to join the officers and men of the British Army and experience their life at first hand.

Opposite page: The Trigat MR is an international collaboration project for a medium-range, infantry-portable, laser-guided anti-tank missile. With a range of between 50 and 2,000 metres, Trigat MR is capable of destroying all known armour. If ordered it will replace Milan.

Above: Trigat LR is the long-range anti-tank missile capable of being fitted to a vehicle or helicopter. It is designed to be a fire and forget missile with a range of 4-5 kilometres. As such, it is intended as a replacement for the Swingfire and TOW in British Army use. One proposal for the armoured vehicle application is to fit the sight and missiles on to a platform at the end of a 12m folding mast.

Below: When describing the role of the future Army one should remember that it has a valuable non-combat role in assisting the civil authorities during an emergency. We are fortunate in this country in that, as a rule, we do not suffer from natural disasters, but all countries suffer from man-made ones. Many troops helped in the recovery of the aircraft's remains following the terrorist bomb action over Lockerbie. The appearance on the streets of many cities of service fire crews and, more recently, ambulance crews, during strikes has ensured emergency cover.

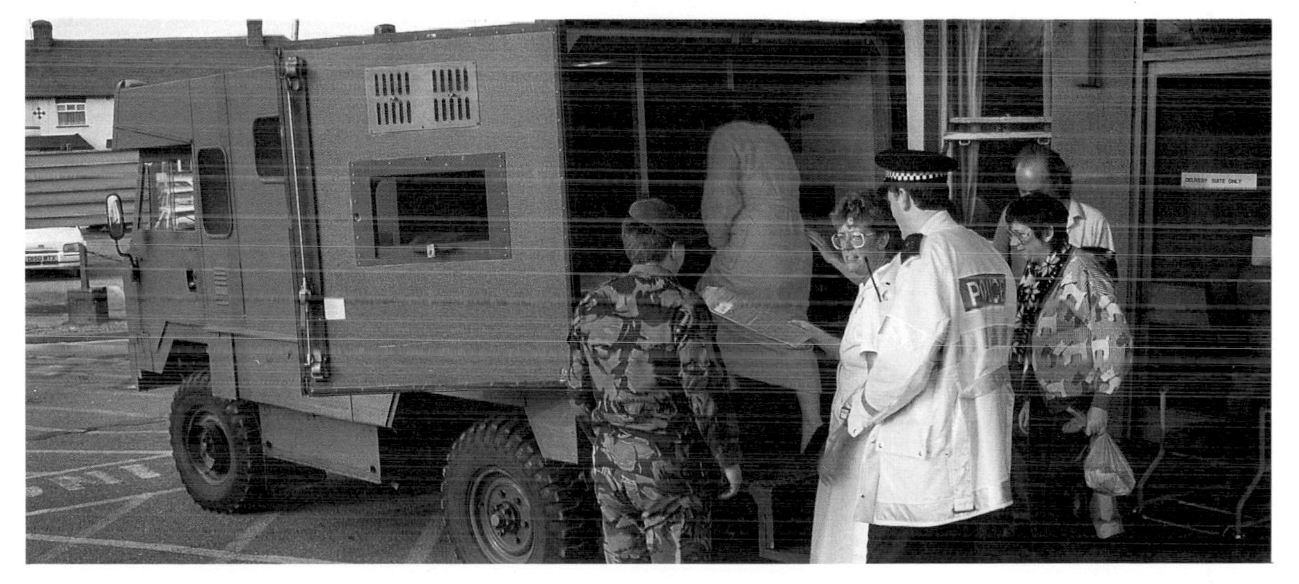

UKLF

United Kingdom Land Forces (UKLF) is responsible for the defence of the UK and has a force of some 100,000 regular, TA and reserve personnel available in an emergency.

UKLF has its headquarters at Wilton from where it commands the various peacetime Military Districts into which the country is split. In addition it is responsible for the training establishments which will provide the regular soldiers not only for the UK but also BAOR and the overseas regiments. In wartime the training establishments would become active units supporting a number of infantry brigades which provide the backbone of the UK's defence.

The UKLF provides a base for the three Infantry Brigades of 2nd Infantry Division and 19 Infantry Brigade which would deploy to Germany and become part of 1 (BR) Corps in time of tension or war.

1 Infantry Brigade is earmarked to the Commander Allied Command Europe (ACE) as a central reserve for NATO. It also forms part of the UK Mobile Force contribution to the AMF which could be deployed to Norway or Turkey to strengthen the NATO flanks.

5 Airborne Brigade at Aldershot is administered by UKLF and provides the Army with its Para capability. As well as providing defensive capability for the UK, 5 Airborne Brigade provides a quick reaction force able to deploy to anywhere in the world to protect British interests.

Left: A mounted trooper wearing Mounted Review Dress at Horse Guards Parade. The steel cuirass of breast and back plates worn by the Life Guards and the Blues and Royals marks them as the last regiments to wear body armour, although this is returning in the form of combat body armour. This form of cuirass dates back to George IV and has not been worn in battle since the late 17th Century. The badge on his arm indicates that he is a regimental signals instructor.

Right: During any period of increased political tension or terrorist activity, civil airports can become a potential target. For this reason troops may be called in to assist the police, who will also be armed, on their security patrols. Their job is to be a highly visible force, and one able to react very quickly to any potential threat. Meanwhile, security will be tightened significantly behind the scenes and many extra checks and procedures will be carried out.

Northern Ireland

Although Northern Ireland is part of the United Kingdom, the situation there is not normal and is therefore treated as a separate area so far as Army administration is concerned.

The Army Headquarters in Northern Ireland is at Lisburn, some ten miles south-west of Belfast, from where the administration of the 10,000 Regular and 6,500 Ulster Defence Regiment (UDR) soldiers based in Northern Ireland is conducted. Command is exercised through three brigade headquarters: 3 Infantry Brigade in Armargh, 8 Infantry Brigade in Londonderry and 39 Infantry Brigade in Lisburn.

Up to 1969 the Army had maintained a garrison of some 2,500 men in Northern Ireland, but on 14 August the Royal Ulster Constabulary (RUC) conceded that their men were no longer able to contain the violence in Belfast and Londonderry and the Government decided to change its security policy. As a result the General Officer Commanding (GOC) – a Lieutenant-General – assumed responsibility for all security operations including those carried out by the Police. This resulted in an increase within twelve months to 13,000 men. At its peak during Operation 'Motorman', when the republican 'no-go' areas in Belfast and Londonderry were cleared, numbers reached more than 21,000.

By 1977 the RUC had recovered sufficiently to take the lead in security matters and the Army's role reverted to one of support. Within twelve months the Security Force level had fallen to 13,000, and to 9,000 by 1985. In 1986, following a rise in terrorist activity, the strength of the Army rose to its current level. The degree of support required for the police is minimal in much of Northern Ireland, but is greater in the troubled areas such as West Belfast and some border areas.

For emergency situations an infantry battalion in the UK is always on stand-by. This reserve, known as the Spearhead Battalion, is rotated so to provide an emergency force that can be deployed anywhere, not just in Northern Ireland.

Opposite page, left: Soldiers patrolling the streets of Belfast is a fairly regular sight. Working in support of The Royal Ulster Constabulary (RUC), they provide a high-profile armed escort to enable the police to carry out their everyday duties despite the ever-present threat from terrorists.

Opposite page, right: Foot patrols in deeply sectarian areas of Belfast must maintain a very high state of alertness. The terrorists have many sympathizers and may have a hold on the local inhabitants. Hideaways enable them to shoot and run, or plant explosives with impunity. These attacks in built-up areas are carried out with scant regard for the innocents who sustain injury and damage.

Above: The FV1611, known as the Pig, evolved from the Humber 1-ton truck which was converted for the Armoured Personnel Carrier (APC) role as a stop-gap while awaiting deliveries of the FV603 Saracen. In total some 1,700 were built.

Subsequent events in Northern Ireland brought a reprieve for the Pig which had been declared obsolete. Its size made it reasonably successful, providing a safe visible presence without being too obtrusive.

By 1972 the terrorists had access to high-velocity armour-piercing bullets which could penetrate the Pig's armour, so some 500 of the vehicles were up-armoured together with several other additions.

In 1984 the last of the Saracens were withdrawn from operational use and their role was completely taken over by the Pig, which had received additional modifications over the years. This vehicle has been covered with a structure to give protection against RPG-7 anti-tank missiles.

Below: Glover Webb have produced a number of armoured vehicles for use in Northern Ireland. Based on the 110 Land Rover, this vehicle is armoured and has a roof hatch and double rear doors. This patrol are equipped with the SA80 and have protective visors fitted to their helmets.

Left: The Glover Webb armoured Land Rover out in West Belfast as part of the high-visibility patrols. Besides supporting the Royal Ulster Constabulary, the object of the patrols is to give visible reassurance to the civilians and offer a warning to the terrorists. The armoured Land Rover enables the patrol to reach a trouble-spot reasonably quickly and gives them some protection once they arrive.

Below left: On patrol in Northern Ireland, live ammunition is carried for self-defence. Safety is of paramount consideration when handling weapons and live ammunition, so when a patrol returns to base weapons are unloaded and checked, and all ammunition that has been issued must be accounted for.

Below: Because of the indiscriminate nature of terrorist attacks in

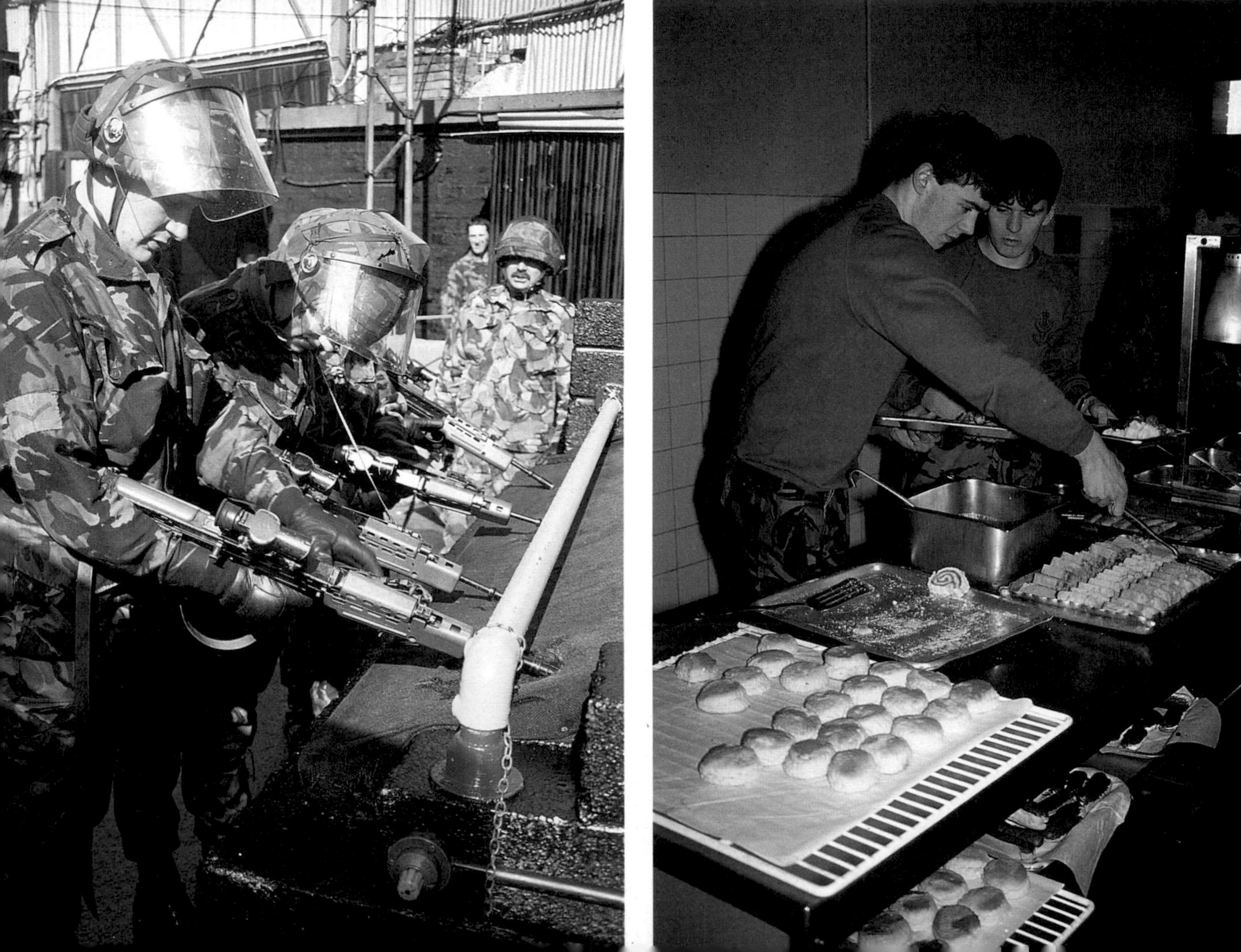

Northern Ireland, the presence of large numbers of troops socializing in the evenings at local pubs creates a potential target. As a result troops in Northern Ireland usually stay within their compounds when not on patrol. To keep up morale a wide range of activities and entertainment is provided, including sport, and of course food in the Mess, produced by the Army Catering Corps.

Above: A number of Army Air Corps (AAC) helicopters are maintained in Northern Ireland to support the security operation. In the main these are the Lynx – used mainly for troop movements – and the Gazelle AH.1, as seen here, which is used for a variety of roles including communications, small troop deployments, medivac and observation. In the latter role various items of surveillance equipment can be installed to enable the Gazelle to be positioned some distance away from the suspected target but still able to observe in detail.

Right: When on patrol, the soldiers are effectively on their own. Although in communication with back-up forces, if trouble arises they will have to fend for themselves until reinforcements arrive. This is when their training will be put to good use. To this end each soldier must carefully prepare, check and then pack his kit ready for patrol.

Left: Two soldiers move out of their quarters to join their colleagues on a patrol which could last from four hours to four days. Because of the terrorist threat, blast walls surround buildings and most windows have protective covering inside.

Below: Members of a patrol wait for their transport which can be a land vehicle or a helicopter. The helicopter is fast and less vulnerable to ambush than a land vehicle, but its noise betrays the presence of the troops.

Above: Once out on patrol the means of travel is by the Mark 1 foot and for which footwear has improved as a result of lessons learned during the Falklands Campaign. The patrol is basic soldiering with the section watching, looking, listening and remaining constantly alert.

Above right: When a suspected target has been spotted the section commander has to decide on his course of action. Depending on the threat level and the patrol brief, this may require radioing for reinforcements. Alternatively it may mean the patrol going to ground, applying full camouflage and observing. For this soldier, carrying the radio may be extra weight, but he will be the corner-stone of the comms.

Right: The Ulster Defence Regiment (UDR) is the youngest and largest Infantry Regiment in the British Army. Recruiting commenced on 1 January 1970 and the Regiment was declared operational on 1 April 1970.

The UDR has played a vital part in military operations in Northern Ireland. It consists of nine battalions which provide police support for 80 per cent of the Province. It is made up of about 3,000 full-time soldiers and a further 3,000 part-timers who can be called up for full-time duty should the situation require. In 1990 the 7th/10th (City of Belfast), UDR received the Wilkinson Sword of Peace in recognition of its valuable contribution towards establishing good relations with the local community.

Members of 4th (County of Fermanagh) Battalion are seen here dealing with a suspicious car. A common occurrence, it is usually the result of an innocent driver leaving his car parked carelessly.

Left: An extremely useful tool in the EOD inventory is Wheelbarrow – a tracked, remotely controlled vehicle on which a range of specialist tools and cameras are fitted. Over the last decade and a half Wheelbarrow has increased in sophistication and can now include in addition to conventional cameras, X-Ray, low light and thermal-imaging (TI) cameras. While of limited use in dealing with Second World War explosives, Wheelbarrow is a vital tool for the anti-terrorist EOD teams, now that suspect packages can contain a variety of lethal explosives.

Below: The disrupter can be a simple cutting tool for severing cables, or an explosive charge which will destroy the detonating device before it activates. While Wheelbarrow is useful on many occasions, the EOD crew still have to dismantle the device themselves but can at least be correctly prepared. Wheelbarrow has saved numerous EOD crews from serious injury or death. During the troubles in Northern Ireland EOD crews have been called out to well in excess of 40,000 incidents. The Wheelbarrow seen here belongs to the Belfast Detachment 321 EOD Company RAOC and is seen investigating a suspicious car.

The Paras

The soldiers of The Parachute Regiment have the reputation of being supermen, partly because of their extremely tough training and the fierce demands made of them by the Regiment. During a Para assault all available equipment will be air dropped which means that the Para will have a limited amount of ammunition and only the Light Gun for artillery assault. This in contrast to the infantry soldier who can call up further supplies when running low on ammunition, or request an artillery barrage from the rear. So the Para must use his ammunition economically. When on the move the infantryman will usually have transport in the form of the Warrior or Saxon. The Paras have a few Land Rovers but these are likely to be used to carry heavy kit; more often than not the Para will have to walk to his objective. The Paras' 'yomp' across the Falklands has now become almost legendary.

To assess new recruits a week of punishing endurance tests has been formulated. Such is the intensity of the tests that twelve weeks of training are undertaken to prepare the recruits. The officers and men who wish to join the Regiment or become Paras within 5 Airborne Brigade have a three-weeks course but all have to pass the same test. For those wishing to become Paras from 5 Airborne Brigade the brigade organizes a three-weeks preparation course.

The test begins on day one with a 2.6km obstacle course followed by a 2.8km log-carrying race. The day is completed with one minute of milling (fighting with controlled aggression). Day two features a 16km speed march followed by a confidence course and then a 1.2km obstacle course. Day three comprises a 28km endurance march. Day four is devoted to an individual 15km route march followed by an individual 10km speed march. Day five sees a 12km stretcher race. On successfully completing the recruit receives his red beret and is then off to commence the next stage of his training which is his parachute course.

Right: After the strenuous ground training, there follows a four-weeks course at the RAF No 1 Parachute Training School (No 1 PTS) at RAF Brize Norton, to instil the necessary procedures and safety drills. During this period of training the Para Recruit is taken to RAF Weston on the Green where he is introduced to the balloon car – a wicker basket suspended below a barrage balloon.

Left: The balloon ascends to 800 feet and the time comes for the last few days of training to be put into effect. The instructor opens the safety bar and the first recruit steps forward. On the instruction 'Go!' the trainee steps over the edge and drops some 200 feet until the parachute begins to break his fall. Once the parachute has opened there are only a couple of minutes left to steer himself away and prepare for the landing. A further eight jumps from a Hercules are required before the presentation of the coveted Para wings.

Below: At RAF Lyneham, the Paras' aircraft, the Hercules, are prepared. Here members of 47 Air Despatch (47AD) prepare a Medium Stressed Platform (MSP) in which a Land Rover and Light Gun have been loaded. The MSP allows a wide permutation of kit requirements to be pre-loaded ready for the drop. A variety of shock-absorbing materials are used to try to ensure that the load receives negligible damage on impact with the ground.

Right: Properly rigged, loaded and checked, the MSP is stored ready for the drop. While the Paras are making their final checks to their equipment and briefings are being carried out, the aircraft are prepared. Part of the formation will be carrying the MSPs and these are loaded into the Hercules along a roller track.

Right: Shortly before engines are started the Paras don all their kit and are driven or walk out to their allocated aircraft. The RAF flies two basic versions of the Hercules: the C.1, which can carry 64 fully equipped Paras, and the C.3 90.

Right: Some 24 hours before the drop a single aircraft will drop the Pathfinder Platoon using the High Altitude Low Opening (HALO) parachute system. This will entail a team of highly trained and experienced Paras free-falling from some 18,000 feet, and not opening their parachutes until at low altitude so as to avoid detection. Once on the ground the Pathfinders will undertake a recce of the DZ as a final check. A signal will be sent back to the main force via satellite communications to confirm that the DZ is secure.

Right: Aboard the Hercules the Paras are accommodated in four rows of canvas and webbing seats which run lengthways down the aircraft. As the aircraft approaches the Dropping Zone (DZ) the Paras undergo their final checks before attaching their static lines to one of the pair of wires running the length of the aircraft.

Below left: Allowances having been made for wind speed and direction, once over the DZ the Wedge is released from the ramp on the Hercules (visible with white parachute) and is immediately followed by the Paras jumping from the side doors. The Wedge is a 1-tonne container of immediately required supplies.

Top right: The drop can take as little as three and a half minutes until the last man is on the ground. From 800 feet the stream of RAF Hercules would now revert to the transit height of 250 feet for the return to base.

Bottom right: A short distance out from the DZ, Hercules split into two streams. The main stream will drop the Paras, the second, with the MSPs, will fly slightly off-set to ensure that the loads do not get mixed up with the men on landing, and so causing possible injuries.

Each Hercules can carry two MSPs which have a small parachute to pull them out of the aircraft and a number of large ones which deploy when the load is clear. As they drop, large air bags inflate on the underside of the MSP; these burst on impact to help absorb the landing shock.

Left: Once the Paras have dropped, teams make their way straight to the MSP DZ for de-rigging. It is important to get away quickly from the DZ which may soon become a target for enemy forces. For this reason the MSP has been designed to be strong so as to be able to contain the load without breaking on landing, light – so as not to add a significant weight penalty and reduce the useful load carried, and easily dismantled, so that the load can be easily and quickly removed.

Below: Size and weight are a major problem for airborne forces. One answer is the Supacat 6x6 All Terrain Mobile Vehicle with its ability to traverse routes inaccessible to many other vehicles. Although a low ground pressure vehicle it can carry six fully equipped men or a payload of 1,000 kilograms. Each vehicle has an electrical winch

which will enable it to self-load air-dropped pallets. It is also capable of towing the Light Gun or similar weapons. It has a road speed of 48km/hr and an amphibious capability.

Right: With air dropping being the final option to commanders, the choice of DZ can be difficult. Dropping on to the objective can present the element of surprise, but will mean that inevitably the men will be spread out – perhaps too thinly. To use a DZ a few kilometres away from the objective may retain the element of surprise, and will give the Paras time to re-group and ensure that the attack plans are implemented in the correct sequence. However, the enemy may have been alert and have had some time to prepare his counter-attack. The final choice will depend on Intelligence received about the enemy. Whatever the decision the Paras are well trained in crossing long distances on foot with full kit. The 'Yomp' during the Falkland Campaign by 2 and 3 Para across the island proved their fitness and provided the element of surprise by doing the unexpected.

Below right: A vital part of any Operation or Exercise is to provide the current SITREP (SITuation REPort) and the future plans for the Officers and Section Commanders. These normally take the form of the CO briefing his Officers about the next Phase. This information would be passed to Section Commanders and finally to the men.

Left: Land Rovers are the main vehicles used by the Paras for an air drop because of their size and versatility. Here one of the Land Rovers has been fitted out with signals equipment to provide The Brigade Command VHF comms net for the Brigade Tactical HQ.

Below left: Once the LPBG (Leading Parachute Battalion Group) has landed it will hope to clear an airhead as soon as possible. This may have been the primary objective. The airhead may be an existing airfield or a suitable area of ground. Depending on when the LPBG has secured its immediate area it can be reinforced by the FUPBG (Follow Up Parachute Battalion Group), which is of similar make-up and may also be air-dropped or air-landed.

Once the area is considered secure Hercules will air land the rest of the Brigade. This will include a wide range of additional troops, armoured and soft-skinned vehicles, and support elements including Engineers, Ordnance, Signals, Army Air Corps and Medical units. Here a member of the REME can be seen diagnosing a failed printed circuit board in a specialized repair vehicle.

Top right: The Eager Beaver is a rough terrain fork-lift tractor which is widely used by the Army. Air-dropped as part of the Logistics Cell, this vehicle will be used to collect and assemble the 1-tonne pallets, of which up to twenty can be part of the initial drop, and a further 130 tonnes of Combat Supplies which make up the LPBG requirement. The Eager Beaver can lift a maximum of 1,814 kilograms.

Bottom right: As the Operation or Exercise proceeds the airhead will become progressively busier as aircraft bring in more troops and supplies. The aircraft are most likely to be the RAF Hercules, but depending on the scale of the operation there may be other air forces or charter aircraft involved. On this airhead an RAF Hercules is being unloaded of ammunition which is being stockpiled ready for onward transmission by land or helicopter to the front line.

04
FZ
59

Above: A vital element of 5 Airborne Brigade are the Royal Engineers who have a wide range of support functions, one of which being to deny the enemy freedom of movement. This can be achieved in various ways, from either blowing or placing trip explosives on bridges, to various forms of mines.

A conventional minefield takes a long time to prepare which may not be available to the Paras. A weapon system which can be utilized is the Ranger mine-layer. This system can be mounted on the back of a Stalwart, 4-tonne truck or Combat Assault Boat, but is more likely to be fitted on to a FV432. The Ranger system consists of a rack of 72 disposable tubes each of which contains eighteen anti-personnel mines. As the vehicle moves the tubes can be fired at a rate of up to one a second which distributes the mines randomly over a range of more than 150 metres.

Left: The Ranger mine system has a

training variant which is to all intents identical with the live system, except that it fires a plastic inert version which can be collected and re-used. Alternatively a compressed peat 'mine' can be used which has no adverse effects on the land used for training and therefore does not need to be retrieved after use.

Above: Because of the weight restrictions imposed on air-mobile forces, 5 Brigade's artillery assets are equipped only with the 105mm L118 Light Gun. They are manned by members of 7 RHA whose initial objective is to remove all their kit from the MSPs and set up at the pre-planned fire points as quickly as possible. From these they can engage enemy positions up to 17,200 metres.

7 RHA has three gun batteries each with six Light Guns. A further troop – P Troop – is also the only parachute air defence troop in Western Europe and is equipped with 12 Javelin missile launchers.

Right: The L118 Light Gun was designed to provide a good range while remaining portable, and is now the standard equipment for UK-based field regiments as well as 5 Brigade. It is a versatile weapon, able to fire a range of ammunition and be highly effective. The 105mm HE round has 70 per cent of the range of the 155mm although the latter is three times the weight. During the final battle in the Falklands up to 400 rounds a day per gun were being fired. In total 17,000 rounds were fired by the 30 Light Guns with no major equipment failures being reported.

Left: The speed and efficiency of the handlers is vital because an aircraft on the ground is a sitting target. Additionally, there is little point in having a large stock of supplies if an urgently required item cannot be located quickly. A large area of stores can provide an ideal target for a planned or opportunist air attack.

The requirement for munitions will escalate as events progress. Initially the LPBG can last for some three days with rifle, machine-gun and mortar ammunition provided in fifteen 1-tonne containers. However, when 7 (Para) RHA begin to use their 105mm Light Gun they could require 22 1-tonne containers of ammunition for a similar period.

Left: As the battle progresses a river may provide an obstacle because there is no suitable bridge or it has been blown by the enemy. An Air-Portable Bridge can be flown in by Hercules and parachuted to the Paras, to be moved to the required location by Land Rover. All the components of this modular system are man-portable. A team of sixteen men can build a 15.2m clearspan bridge in approximately twenty minutes. An alternative use for the system is as a powered raft or floating bridge.

Left: As soon as contact is made with the enemy the possibility exists that prisoners of war (POW) will be taken. A system must be quickly up and running to cater for potential detainees or the conflict could become bogged down with front-line forces holding prisoners.

Right: At the airhead provision is made for the reception of all captured enemy and suspected enemy. Here they will be interrogated. To reduce the manpower required to control and secure them, detainees will probably be flown out on the re-supply Hercules to another POW camp well away from the conflict.

Right: Another vital provision that must be set up as soon as possible is a field hospital, provided by the Royal Army Medical Service. The size and capabilities of this facility will be proportional to the perceived requirement. For a quick rescue of hostages it might not exist at all, any casualties being treated aboard the returning aircraft. At the other extreme, the recent Gulf War dictated a massive field hospital capacity for large numbers of anticipated casualties. Fortunately they were not required.

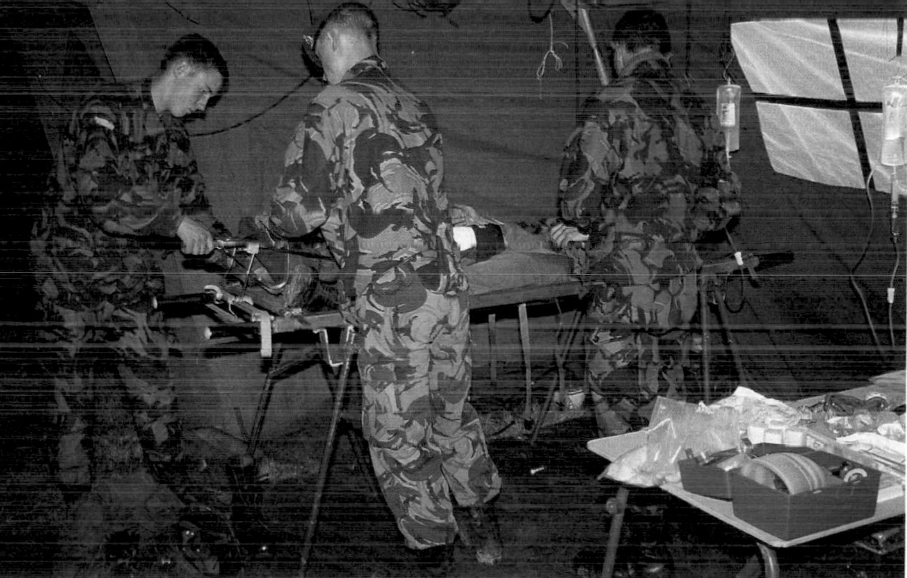

Right: All field hospitals will run on the same principle, only the amount of facilities at their disposal being variable. The field medics will have administered first aid to the casualty. On arriving at the field hospital by vehicle or helicopter the casualty will be checked for NBC (Nuclear, Chemical or Biological) contamination should the threat have existed. Any positive result will have to be neutralized before the extent of the injury can be assessed and treated. Once the casualty has stabilized he can be flown out to conventional hospital facilities.

24 Airmobile Brigade

24 Brigade was formed in 1914 as part of 8th Division. Over the years it has been renamed and its role has changed a number of times. In 1988 24 Infantry Brigade was retitled 24 Airmobile Brigade to reflect its new role, and was based at Catterick.

The Brigade's primary role is to act as an anti-tank reserve force for rapid deployment with NATO forces in Europe. It is equipped with a Lynx AH.7 Regiment fitted with TOW anti-tank missiles together with Milan and 94mm LAW-equipped Infantry Battalions. It is assisted by the RAF Support Helicopter Force equipped with two Squadrons of Chinooks and a further two Squadrons of Pumas.

The concept of 24 AMB is to provide a rapidly deployable force that can be placed astride the main axis of a possible enemy break-through. Using its powerful anti-tank capability, 24 AMB will destroy advancing armour until friendly forces are able to launch a counter movement to restore the front line. This action may be achieved by the Airmobile Combat Engineers laying mines to force the enemy along a route that will provide a better opportunity for destroying their armour.

The Options for Change group the mobile forces (i.e., the Paras, the Royal Marines, the ACE Mobile Force and the 24 AMB) as a new strategic reserve division. This will also include an armoured brigade and be used to react to 'out of area' crises as well as throughout the NATO region. Time will show how this will be implemented.

The 24 AMB Infantry component comprises the 1st Battalion The Duke of Edinburgh's Royal Regiment and the 1st Battalion The Gloucester-

Left: One of the problems 24 AMB has is of logistics. With the call to deploy an effective force against an enemy who has already gained the initiative by moving first, time is needed to get into position with minefields laid; the efficient moving of men, equipment and supplies takes time. To lay an effective anti-tank minefield takes time, but a way has been found to reduce this.

A Chinook can airlift three pallets of Bar Mines to the required location and then distribute them via a chute while hover taxiing. The Engineers of 51 Field Squadron seen here have only the task of concealing and arming the mines, the laborious task of humping them over fields has been eliminated. The Bar Mine can be fitted with a variety of fuzes to provide various effects and also complicate the job of the enemy sappers trying to breach the minefield.

Above: RAF Chinook and Puma helicopters provide the airlift capability for 24 AMB. In a fluid conflict the speed of reaction of the Brigade to an enemy advance can affect its result. The force of four Chinooks and two Pumas can rapidly move more than 150 troops together with their equipment including vehicles.

shire Regiment, which are due to merge as part of the defence cuts announced in July 1991, plus 1st Battalion The Green Howards. The three Companies are equipped with thirty Milan posts, a Fire Support Company with nine 81mm Mortars plus twelve Milan posts, a Recce Platoon and an HQ Company.

24 AMB has 9 Regiment, Army Air Corps to provide its airborne anti-tank capability. It comprises three Squadrons of Lynx AH.7 – Nos 656, 657, 672 Squadrons. Each Lynx can carry eight TOW anti-tank missiles which have an effective range of 3,750 metres. Sixteen of the improved Lynx Mk 9 utility helicopter are now entering service.

Above: The Chinook HC.1 is capable of carrying up to 44 men. It is fitted with a tail ramp for quick access but can also be used for loading freight or small vehicles. Troops can be seen here deploying from the Chinook with their Milan posts and missiles.

Left: The Puma HC.1 is the RAF's other helicopter which it flies in support of the Army. Although of lesser capacity, the Puma is also capable of carrying underslung freight with loads of up to 2,500 kilograms which can include a Light Gun or ammunition. It has a capacity for up to twenty fully equipped men, which means that a flight of Pumas could swiftly move a sizeable force from 24 AMB into position to stem an enemy breakthrough.

Above: Once at the location the troops jump from the helicopter with all their kit. On the ground the helicopter is vulnerable and so the crew will be keen to be airborne again and on to the next task. Meanwhile the Milan sections will move quickly into their positions ready to stem an enemy advance.

Below: By rapidly laying minefields 24 AMB would be able to force an advancing enemy through a funnel of ground which would provide easy targets for the variety of anti-tank weapons at the Brigade's dispoal.

It is unlikely that once an enemy has committed himself to advance that he will have sufficient time effectively to deal with a minefield. Thus, once his forces are exposed they would be forced to move through what would seem to them to be the weakest point. Here a USAF A-10 Thunderbolt 'tank-buster' joins in the attack against advancing enemy armour.

Above: One of 24 AMB's main anti-tank weapons is Milan. While most BAOR infantry battalions are equipped with 24 firing posts, because of its role 24 AMB is equipped with 40.

Milan is a French/German weapon designed by Euromissile and was ordered for the British Army in 1978. A total of 60,000 missiles were built by BAe Dynamics for the British Army together with 836 launcher posts. From the outset Milan was designed to be relatively light and can be broken down into two-man portable sections. In addition to Milan, 24 AMB infantry are also equipped with 94mm LAW.

Below: The Milan system consists of the firing post or launcher and the missile. The launcher contains the optical guidance system which is now fitted with the MIRA thermal-imaging sight for low light or smoke conditions. It also doubles as protection for the firer. The missile comes in sealed tubes which simply clip on to the launcher.

Once a target has been located and the operator has taken aim the missile is launched. This fires a gas generator which blows the missile out of the tube at 75m/sec. At the same time it ejects the tube to the rear of the launcher. Once clear of the launcher the rocket motor fires and the missile is controlled via a fine guidance wire making it impossible to jam. The Milan has a minimum range of 400 metres and a maximum of 1,950 metres.

Right: Besides using the Lynx in the anti-tank role, it can also be used for carrying up to ten soldiers together with their equipment. As a utility helicopter it can have many additional roles including casualty evacuation, liaison, and cargo-carrying including underslung loads.

Above right: The second anti-tank weapon used by 24 AMB is the Westland Lynx which is widely used in the British Army. It is fitted with eight TOW missiles on pylons each side of the fuselage. TOW is a wire-guided, optically tracked missile that was designed in the USA.

The Lynx would normally work in conjunction with the Gazelle which would act as the spotter.

Once a suitable target has been identified the Lynx would be brought forward. As the enemy commence their attack and encounter the minefields which have been laid, the attacking armour will become concentrated thus providing an ideal area for the Lynx to work. Hovering behind cover the weapon aimer will identify the target in his thermal-imaging sight then fire the TOW. The sight is gyroscopically stabilized and as long as the graticules are kept on target the system will ensure a hit.

In 1990 the Ministry of Defence ordered 24 of the Mk 9 Battlefield Lynx for 24 AMB – sixteen being new and eight being modified from Mk 7. Besides the obvious swapping of the skid undercarriage for wheels, the Lynx Mk 9 is fitted with composite blades which provide extra performance allowing the all-up weight to increase to 5,126 kilograms. They will also reduce vibration which is a problem to a greater or lesser degree on all helicopters, creating maintenance difficulties as well as crew fatigue.

Left: The dispatch-rider on his motorcycle still remains an important means of communication despite all modern systems. In an ECM environment or if radio contact is poor, the motorcycle can be the most secure form of communication. In this electronic age when computers are widely used at all levels of command the movement of information, possibly on floppy disks, can be vital. This member of 24 AMB is using the Armstrong MT500 motorcycle for his role.

Left: The ROC Bar Mine has been designed to replace the Mk 7 anti-tank mine. Unlike any other British mine in shape, the Bar Mine increases the likelihood of being activated because of its length. The track from any vehicle will be destroyed if it hits the Bar Mine, while a tank will have its body armour damaged. A variety of fuzes is available; these are activated automatically when being laid by the towed Bar minelayer which is the normal method of laying. It is usually towed behind the FV432 but can be operated by many other vehicles including a Land Rover. The Bar mine can be laid by hand for which a four-mine pack is available.

Right: The Chinook has three underslung load points to which a variety of loads can be attached: fuel or water cells, two Light Guns or pallets of ammunition. In fact more than 11,000 kilograms of external freight can be carried.

The Chinook proved to be a valuable asset during the Falkland Campaign and the Gulf War. Only one was available in the Falklands, enemy action having destroyed the others aboard *Atlantic Conveyor*, but it did exceptional work, carrying loads well in excess of its peacetime restrictions, including moving 81 fully equipped men on a vital mission – 37 more than the normal maximum.

Infantry

The Infantry provide the main manpower of the British Army. Their role is to hold ground and to help them do this they are equipped with a variety of equipment and vehicles. The old style of infantry digging itself in remains when positions have to be held, but the quality of the weaponry has advanced dramatically.

Milan and 94mm LAW missiles have been issued for anti-tank protection. CLAW was acquired for use in the Gulf War to provide anti-personnel capability for the infantryman in addition to mortars. For many years the FV432 APC has provided protection for infantry on the move and some 1,240 remain in service. Added to these are 532 FV103 Spartan APC from the Scorpion family of vehicles. The FV432 is in the process of being replaced by 1,048 Warrior and 664 Saxon. The 7.62mm SLR is being replaced by orders for 332,000 of the lighter, 5.56mm SA80 Individual Weapon (IW) and Light Support Weapon (LSW). For protection against NBC weapons the S10 General Service Respirator together with suit has been provided. The old webbing carrying equipment is being replaced by the Personal Load Carrying Equipment (PLCE).

Until recently there were 55 infantry battalions but the 1991 Defence Cuts reduces these to 38. Much of this will be achieved by the merging of some regiments thus bringing them up to normal strength.

Right: A number of years ago, while the Cold War was still a real threat and the off area training exercises in Germany were becoming more politically sensitive, a decision was made to build a replica German village on Salisbury Plain. This has been completed and enables Fighting In Built Up Areas (FIBUA) training to be undertaken without disruption of civilian life. While the threat has reduced dramatically over the last couple of years, this type of training environment will always be required.

Left: The 7.62mm General-Purpose Machine-gun L7A2 or GPMG has been the standard machine-gun with the Army since the early 1960s. Developed from the Belgian FN MAG, the GPMG is a compromise between a heavy and a light machine-gun. In practice it is rather weighty with its bipod for the light role, and suffers from barrel overheating in the heavy role. Having said that the GPMG is a solid design which has proved to be reliable. As a result it is widely used by the infantry although it is being replaced in the light support role by the Light Support Weapon of the SA80 family.

Below: When operating in the heavy or Sustained Fire (SF) role the GPMG can be fired at double the light rate (200rpm instead of 100rpm). Its maximum effective range is also much greater – 1,800 metres as opposed to 800 metres. This is achieved by the use of a buffered tripod which can be located in, for example, the back of a Land

Rover for high mobility. Although each section has two LSWs, each company will keep three GPMGs for the SF role.

Above left: A vital part of the infantry battalion is the Fire Support Company which contains the anti-tank platoon. While they are equipped with 24 Milan firing posts, the Mechanized Company will have its own additional anti-tank weapon in the form of 94mm LAW (Light Anti-tank Weapon).

94mm LAW is a single-shot rocket with a more advanced and effective HEAT warhead which can penetrate armour more than 650mm thick. It weighs 9.6 kilograms and is supplied in a sealed container. When required for use the tube is extended, end covers removed and the LAW is ready. The launcher tube has an integral shoulder rest, firing grip and sight. It is fitted with a five-round aiming rifle whose ammunition produces a small flash when hitting a solid object. Once fired the tube is simply discarded.

Above right: The Carl Gustav is a Swedish-designed 84mm anti-tank weapon which has been made in the UK. Normally operated by a crew of two, one man loading and the other aiming and firing, the Carl Gustav can be operated by one man. It can penetrate up to 228mm of armour, but like the 66mm HEAT, is being replaced by the 94mm LAW for greater effect.

Below: The Luchaire 40mm CLAW (CLose Assault Weapon) was brought into service with the British Army at short notice for the Gulf War and proved to be highly effective. It was purchased to satisfy a requirement that was highlighted during the Falklands Campaign for a HEAT/AP weapon, but because of various defence cuts never satisfied.

In British Army service CLAW is designated L75A1 and is a rifle-launched grenade issued to some infantry units. It was issued to some units in Northern Ireland in July 1991 to combat the reinforced vehicle attacks by terrorists. The L75A1 clips on to the muzzle of an unmodified SA80 and is aimed by a sight fitted to the top of the SUSAT sight. On squeezing the trigger a normal round of ammunition is fired into the base of the grenade; this transfers its kinetic energy, simultaneously firing the grenade's booster charge. The L75A1 has an effective range of 125 metres and is capable of burning through the armour of light and medium vehicles as well as having a fragmentation outer layer for the anti-personnel role. Once fired the SA80 can fire normally or fire additional grenades without any alteration.

The advantage of the L75A1 is that the effective range of the grenade has been increased by more than 100 metres over the conventional hand-grenade as well as having an anti-armour capability. This soldier has the L75A1 fitted to his SA80 and has two additional rounds in a pouch on the new 90 Pattern Webbing. In addition he is wearing body armour.

Left: The mortar can be thought of as artillery for the infantry. It is basically a tube down which a bomb is dropped; on reaching the bottom, the bomb hits a striking-pin which sets off the explosive charge, blasting the bomb out of the tube. Until recently the British Army has often relied on incoming information to provide details of range and bearing. With the advent of microcomputer technology, the handheld Morzen fire-control computer can enable each mortar team to fire very quickly on a given target. Such was the destructive power of the mortar during the Second World War that much effort was put into a way of defeating it. This resulted in a radar that can track the bomb in flight and thus calculate the firing point and so bring firepower to bear on that location. The British system is called Cymbeline. It is reasonable to assume that an enemy will be similarly equipped, and the handheld fire-control computer enables the mortar team to move into a firing position, launch several rounds and move to another location within a few minutes before the enemy has a chance to fire at them.

Left: One of the advantages of the mortar is that its low noise and smoke signature enables it to be used without easily being spotted. Its high rate of fire of up to fifteen rounds per minute enables a number of bombs to be fired in quick succession to achieve the element of surprise.

Above: The 81mm Mortar can be fired at the rate of fifteen bombs every minute indefinitely, with a 0.5 per cent error in range and 1.5 mils in line. With the relatively high flight time this will enable a platoon to direct more than 100 rounds on the target in one minute and give the minimum warning to the exposed enemy. To assist in night operations the sight is self-illuminating.

In addition to the 81mm Mortar the Army has a lightweight 51mm Mortar which is carried and can be operated by one man, and can fire HE and smoke rounds up to 800 metres. On exploding these HE rounds fragment and can cause fatalities to a radius of eleven metres.

Below left: While the 51mm Mortar is portable in one piece, the 81mm Mortar is much heavier (37.04 kilograms) and is broken down into three pieces for carrying. Despite this split it is still a lot of weight for the troops to carry and so a variant of the FV432 has been modified to carry the 81mm Mortar and fire it through the main roof hatch. Each mechanized infantry battalion is equipped with six vehicles.

Below right: The 81mm Mortar bomb weighs 4.2 kilograms and can be fired at ranges up to a maximum of 5,650 metres. Three types of live bomb are currently used. The light green is a smoke bomb which contains white phosphorus and provides 60 seconds of dense white smoke. The dark green is the high-explosive (HE) bomb. The plastic horseshoe-shaped discs on the stem of the tail contain the explosive charge which propels the bomb. The white round is the illumination bomb. In addition to these a number of inert drill rounds and practice bombs are in use. The 51mm range of mortar bombs follow similar types, but their range is limited to 800 metres and capacity is lessened.

Above: The Illuminating Bomb contains a magnesium compound which will reach full luminosity within a few seconds. It is suspended by parachute and burns for approximately 35 seconds. By firing a sequence of these bombs the target can be lit up indefinitely.

Below: Milan entered German/French production in the mid 1970s and has since been licence-built in India, Italy and the UK. It is in use in 36 countries and has seen active service in the Chad and Iran/Iraq conflicts plus the Falklands and Gulf with the British Army. Euromissile has developed the Milan 2 which has a larger warhead and capability, but the British Army seem to be opting for the BAe Trigat system as the replacement.

Here the Milan has been fired and the spent tube ejected behind the firing point. The missile has been blasted forwards from the tube into free flight and the rocket motor can be seen cutting in to the left of the picture as the missile glides towards the target.

Right: A development of the Milan has evolved whereby the FV103 Spartan APC is fitted with Milan Compact Turret. This is a variant of the Spartan on which two launch tubes are fitted on to a housing on the top of the hull. This gives support for the mechanized infantry, combining mobility with protection.

Below: The Wombat has virtually been replaced by the Milan although a few still exist. It is used as an anti-tank weapon and has a .50 spotting rifle to assist in aiming. This fired, the tracer shows the trajectory and if the target is hit a small burst of marker smoke is emitted. As the spotting rifle and gun are aligned the main 120mm HESH projectile can be fired immediately. It is important that the aiming be accurate because the considerable back blast of the Wombat renders the firing position very conspicuous and can result in a rapid return of fire. The Wombat has a maximum effective range of 1,100 metres. It is seen here being used by 'Orange' forces in an unorthodox manner, from the back of a Land Rover which will ensure a rapid withdrawal after firing.

35 KG 64

Opposite page, top: The FV432 has been the standard mechanized infantry vehicle since the early 1960s. During the early 1970s the Army was looking for a replacement and consideration was given to a British-built M2 Bradley although GKN had been given a development contract for their MCV-80. Eventually, after extensive trials the MCV-80 was ordered and entered service as the Warrior. This new vehicle is now the basis for a whole family of armoured fighting vehicles of which a number are currently in service. It is powered by a Perkins Rolls-Royce V8 Condor engine which gives it a speed of 75km/hr on roads and its high-performance suspension gives it good rough terrain capabilities.

Left: Not a product of Glasnost but a Warrior depicting 'Orange' forces a little more graphically. The Warrior can carry seven fully armed men and their equipment. For their own protection the troops are strapped into their seats while the Warrior is manoeuvring. The first Warrior was delivered to the Grenadier Guards in the summer of 1987.

Above: The FV432 became the standard Army APC from the mid 1960s. Production was maintained by GKN Sankey for nearly ten years during which some 3,000 FV432s were built. Only four basic types of this vehicle have been built, but design improvements over the years have enabled it to fulfil a wide range of roles. Conceived as an APC to carry ten men plus crew, the 15,280-kilogram FV432 can be used as a mobile mortar platform, ambulance or cargo carrier with minimal conversion. Further variants have been built or converted as command vehicle, recovery, Wavell automated data processing post, battlefield and Cymbeline mortar radars, FACE fire control computers anti-tank guided missile platform as well as mine-laying.

Although being replaced by the Warrior, the FV432 is still used in considerable numbers by a wide variety of formations besides the infantry for whom it was initially intended.

Left: The Saxon APC (Armoured Personnel Carrier) entered production in the mid 1970s as an internal security vehicle for export. It was not until 1984 that the first orders for the British Army were placed. The bulk of the Saxons now in service are for the regular UK-based BAOR reinforcement units, providing them with a protected means of transport to reach forward positions, and to have their own armoured protection once there. The wheeled Saxon is able to travel at speeds of up to 96km/h – faster than the equivalent tracked APCs and without the problem of track wear. In addition, the fuel consumption is far better.

Left: Although not part of the infantry, Royal Pioneer Corps (RPC) recruits are initially trained as infantrymen before beginning their main trade training. Their roles can include infantry duties when stationed in Northern Ireland.

The RPC cover a wide range of tasks throughout the Army, and at any one time about 40 per cent of the RPC may be working directly with other arms. Their main role is involved with materials and stores handling. As a consequence they can be expected to be able to operate a variety of handling equipment from trucks to cranes and fork-lift trucks.

Here members of 518th RPC deploy from RAF Brize Norton by VC.10 to the Gulf under Operation 'Granby' and are being reinforced by other Pioneer Companies including the 187th. There their tasks ranged from providing guards and a Quick Reaction Force to assisting the REME with artisan and plumbing functions.

Recce

In the British Army reconnaissance duties are performed by the Household Cavalry and elements of the Royal Armoured Corps, assisted by the Yeomanry which is manned by the TA.

BAOR has two Medium Reconnaissance Regiments, each having three squadrons of three Reconnaissance Troops with four Scimitars, and a support troop with five Spartans. There are two UK-based regiments whose squadrons are equipped with two Scimitars and two Scorpions. In addition each regiment has a guided-weapon squadron equipped with four troops of four Strikers. Each of the regiments has a range of support vehicles to equip the HQ Squadron, Admin Troop and LAD. One of these regiments would be deployed to BAOR in time of conflict while the other one, based at Tidworth, has to allocate one squadron for the ACE Mobile Force.

The Household Cavalry, based at Windsor, have a dual role in that part of the regiment provides the ceremonial troops, while the remainder is tasked with the reconnaissance role for which it is equipped with the Fox and the Scorpion. In addition, the regiment provides armoured vehicles which deploy to Heathrow and Gatwick for anti-terrorist duties as and when required.

The Yeomanry provide two regiments to back up BAOR with a further three which will stay in the UK in the Home Defence role. The two regiments that are earmarked for BAOR use the Fox, but the three in the UK are equipped with Land Rovers.

Right: The Cavalry equipment has moved by leaps and bounds from its original splendour to today's efficient machines. While keeping many of the old traditions and retaining much of the old dress for ceremonial duties, today's cavalry provides the reconnaissance and armoured regiments of the Army. The knight of yesteryear relied on his horse and suit of armour to keep him from trouble and had the lance and sword for his defensive capability. Today the modern reconnaissance cavalry trooper could be one of a FV101 Scorpion crew armed with a 76mm gun.

Left: While the highly visible part of the Household Cavalry performs its ceremonial duties in and around London, the remainder of the regiment practise their normal soldiering on exercises. Here members of the recently amalgamated Blues and Royals provide guard for their HQ hidden in a wooded area. Until the amalgamation, the Life Guards and the Blues and Royals would rotate between Windsor and Germany every five years. The regiment in Germany would be equipped with the Challenger while that in Windsor would be equipped with Scorpion and Fox to provide the recce element for 5 Airborne Brigade. In addition they are tasked with an anti-terrorist role at Heathrow and Gatwick airports.

Below left: There are two principal reconnaissance vehicles currently used by the Army today. The first is the Combat Vehicle Reconnaissance (Wheeled) CVR(W) FV721 Fox which was developed from the 'Big Wheeled Ferret' back in 1965. The first production vehicles came off the production line in 1973 as a replacement for some of the Ferrets.

The Fox is equipped with the same turret as the Scimitar which has the 30mm Rarden cannon plus a 7.62mm co-axial machine-gun. The Rarden can fire either single rounds or bursts of up to six rounds. Ninety-nine rounds of 30mm ammunition can be stowed and these are loaded in clips of three. On firing, the empty cartridge cases are automatically ejected outside the vehicle. Manned by a crew of three, the Fox is capable of 104km/h and it has a good cross-country capability.

Seen here during a recce patrol exercise, this Fox of the Blues and Royals is in the FIBUA training area. The Fox can effectively use its turn of speed to get itself out of trouble if necessary.

Above: The second principal recce vehicle is the FV101 Scorpion, one of a number of designs to meet the Combat Vehicle Reconnaissance requirement. Alvis were given an order for seveteen prototypes in 1967 followed by a production order in 1969. The army currently has 293 Scorpions, 177 of which are currently UK-based. Further orders followed from Belgium, Iran and Saudi Arabia.

The Scorpion is constructed of welded aluminium armour and weighs 7,960 kilograms. It is air portable, two vehicles fitting into the Hercules. The Scorpion has a crew of three. The driver is seated in the front left of the hull, the commander is in the turret as is the gunner. The Scorpion is fitted with a 76mm gun as well as a 7.62mm machine-gun which can be used as a ranging gun if required.

A vital task during any conflict is to ensure that all weapons are clean, oiled and functioning efficiently. During breaks in and at the end of exercises the first task is to work on the weapons. Here the other half of the troops from the Household Cavalry – the Life Guards – practise their skills on an exercise.

Above: The art of camouflage is an ancient craft used to disguise an object, make it invisible, or blend it in with the background. Alternatively it can be used to change the shape of an object and make it look like something else. Here members of the Life Guards drape hessian around the sides of their Fox while parked-up on exercise.

Below: Camouflage is vital to the military. If the enemy is unable to determine exactly what he is going to encounter during an advance or attack he is unlikely to move unless he is sure that his force will be strong enough to meet any situation. If camouflage is good he will be unable fully to identify equipment of defences and this will complicate his plans.

The addition of camouflage has broken up the shape of this Scorpion and it take some identifying at a distance. For the recce platoons good, effective camouflage can enable them to remain close to an enemy position, observe and report while he remains unaware of their presence.

Modern technology in the form of Thermal-Imaging equipment (TI) can help defeat camouflage and smoke-screens by revealing a picture made up of heat signatures. The hotter the object the lighter the image, so metal objects and troops will stand out from the background. By selecting a suitable location and careful camouflage the position of the TI system is less likely to be spotted. To conserve power, it is only used when a threat is perceived.

Opposite page, top left: While most reconnaissance work will be carried out by vehicle, there is still much to be done by the foot-soldier. Although he is more vulnerable when spotted and will not be able to cover such a wide area, he has the advantage of being a small target and able to move quietly and closer to enemy positions. Specialist forces may have additional kit to enable them to work in unsympathetic environments.

Opposite page, top right: The FV105 Sultan manned by members of 13th/18th Royal Hussars (QMO) is the Command Post variant of the Scorpion family of vehicles built by Alvis. It has a much higher hull section because it must accommodate the crew of five or six plus radios, control equipment and map boards.

Opposite page, bottom: Similar to the Scorpion, the FV107 Scimitar is fitted with the 30mm Rarden gun instead of the 76mm gun. While the UK-based armoured reconnaissance regiments use both vehicles in their medium reconnaissance troops, BAOR keep the vehicles in separate troops, the Scimitar being used in the close reconnaissance role.

The Striker is the Anti-Tank Guided Weapon (ATGW) variant of the Scorpion family. Striker can have five Swingfire missiles ready to fire on the top rear of the vehicle and carry a further five units inside the hull. The Swingfire is supplied in a sealed container which only requires plugging in the rack to be ready for firing. Each of these vehicles has a crew of three: commander, driver and gunner, although in the Striker the gunner is the missile controller.

This group contains a selection of all three vehicles from 13th/18th Royal Hussars (QMO) which are about to move off after completion of their exercise.

DANGER
KEEP CLEAR

Right: A convoy of Strikers from 13th/18th Royal Hussars (QMO) moves through a Wiltshire town during Exercise 'Highwayman'. This was the first off training area exercise to be held in the UK for many years, covering the counties of Avon, Dorset, Wiltshire and Gloucestershire.

While this form of exercise has been familiar in Germany, it was new to many in the UK. Although inevitably causing some minor disruptions on the roads, training of this kind is invaluable to the Army. Major training grounds like Salisbury Plain cover extensive areas of land, but after many exercises troops know the lie of the land too well and do not get to stretch their skills as they do in this type of exercise. This is especially true for the recce troops. It may be that in future years, with the reductions from BAOR, more exercises along these lines may be seen once more in this country. Disruption can be kept at a minimum by using Land Rovers as substitutes for some of the tracked vehicles for command and control training.

Right: The FV102 Striker from 13th/18th Royal Hussars (QMO) fires a Swingfire ATGW on the ranges at Otterburn. The Striker is almost identical with the FV103 Spartan APC, but is fitted with five missile racks which remain flush with the top of the hull until firing is imminent. In this configuration it is probable that enemy armour crews and anti-tank helicopters would not perceive it as a high threat until too late.

A total of ten missiles, which have a range of four kilometres, are normally carried by Striker. It can move swiftly into action and be fired remotely from up to 100 metres. This can allow the vehicle to remain hidden while the gunner is forward with a clear view of the target(s).

The Swingfire is a wire-guided missile which entered service in the late 1960s and is currently being upgraded by British Aerospace. Included in the programme is the replacement of the original manual command to line of sight to an automatic command to line of sight system.

Firepower

The main firepower of the British Army is provided by the Royal Artillery and the MBTs (Main Battle Tanks) of the Royal Armoured Corps.

The first two regular companies of British Army artillery were formed in 1716, but artillery had played important parts in prior battles with temporary sections being put together as required and disbanding again. During the First World War the Royal Artillery (RA) expanded to comprise more than 2,000 batteries manned by more than half a million gunners by 1918. With the advent of aircraft the first anti-aircraft units were formed. During the Second World War the RA was again expanded and provided about two-fifths of the Army strength.

Since the war the Artillery has accompanied the British Army to virtually every trouble-spot in which it has been involved, including Korea, Malaysia, Cyrpus, Borneo and recently the Falklands and Gulf.

The Artillery School was formed in 1920 on land which was originally purchased in 1892 and added to in the early 1900s. Its origins were formed from the Horse and Artillery School which relocated at Larkhill during the First World War and the Chapperton Down Artillery School which joined it a short time later. Renamed School of Artillery in 1920, it was soon joined by the Heavy Artillery School and the Siege Artillery School. In 1970 the only RA School not at Larkhill was that at Manobier which provided air defence training and this moved across. The following year the Queen conferred the title 'Royal' on the now complete School.

Today the Royal School of Artillery (RSA) is made up of the Gunnery Wing, Air Defence Wing and the Command and Tactics Wing. In addition there is a REME Wing to look after all the equipment and a Young Officers' Branch. 14 Field Regiment RA is also based at Larkhill to support the School.

One of the main roles of the Royal School of Artillery is to train Regular and Territorial instructors for the RA and to provide the courses for Gunner officers and men as they progress through their careers. The School also provides displays of equipment and firepower demonstrations for other arms and services so as to make the non-artillery units graphically aware of the capabilities of RA firepower as an additional or alternative solution to a military task.

The range of artillery pieces used by the British Army comprises the M107, which has all but disappeared, M110 of which sixteen remain, M109 of which 109 are in service. There are 68 FH70, 151 Abbot, 180 Light Guns, and nine 5.5in Howitzers plus 52 pack Howitzers used for training purposes at the RSA, OTUs. Deliveries of the MLRS are proceeding and an order has been placed for the AS90.

The Royal Armoured Corps has comprised thirteen regiments plus one training regiment based at Bovington. The armoured regiments are either Type 43 or Type 57 depending on the number of MBTs it has on strength. The types of tanks operated by these regiments are the Chieftain of which 752 are still on strength and Challenger of which there are 408. An order has now been placed for the Challenger II and deliveries of these will enter service in the near future to replace some of the older Chieftains.

A number of Royal Armoured Corps regiments will be merging as a result of the 1991 Defence Cuts.

Left: A Royal Navy Sea King is seen here lifting an L118 105mm Light Gun. From 1961 the RA have provided support artillery for the Commandos. The regiment has since been renamed 29th Commando Regiment Royal Artillery. Members of the regiment are all volunteers for the Commando forces and have to pass the tough Commando course before they can wear the coveted green beret.

Below left: FACE is the Field Artillery Computer Equipment used to control artillery firepower. Variables are fed in to the computer including weather, type of projectile, type of weapon, all of which have required laborious calculations in the past. The FACE computer then provides the range and bearing which is passed to the gunners via the AWDATS (Artillery Weapon Data Transmission System).

Below: The advent of the hand-held calculator has reached the artillery in the form of a fire data computer. Built by Zengrange, the Gunzen hand-held artillery fire data computer can handle an 8-gun battery and can store up to 47 target locations plus nine OPs. This speeds up the locating of positions and thus readiness to commence a fire mission. A similar computer, known as the Morzen, is used by mortar teams.

Right: The 105mm Light Gun serves in more than fourteen armies, including the US Army. The fast air mobility of this gun and ease of deployment together with its powerful ammunition make it a very effective weapon.

In action the Light Gun stands on a circular firing platform which allows it to be rapidly traversed through a full 360°. While two members of the crew load the two-part ammunition the third sets the bearing and range.

Right: The normal rate of fire for the Light Gun is six rounds per minute (rpm) although this drops to 3rpm for sustained periods of fire. A rate of 12rpm can be achieved for bursts. The Light Gun has a range of 17 kilometres with standard ammunition and this can be extended up to 21 kilometres with base bleed ammunition. The minimum range of 2,500 metres is achieved by the fitting of a spoiler disc on the nose of the shell to provide a braking action.

Below: It is normal for the 105mm Light Gun to be fired from beneath camouflage nets to try to conceal the weapon, gun crew and ammunition.

The Light Gun was very successful in the Falklands. According to Brigadier Thompson, Commander 3 Commando Brigade, the five Light Gun Batteries were perhaps the winning factor in that war. The ability to bring down concentrated accurate fire crushed the enemy's morale and raised their own. The gunners were able to bring down fire within 50 metres of their own troops during the attack. The artillery proved itself to be the principal killing weapon in the land battle. If properly handled, which it was, it is accurate, instantaneous and devastating. At Darwin/Goose Green there was insufficient artillery and ammunition because the helicopter lift was inadequate. The battle was nearly lost as a result.

Opposite page, top: The decision on DROPS, the Demountable Rack Off-loading and Pick-up System, has taken its time to come to fruition and resulted in the Leyland DAF being ordered. The DROPS concept was originally designed to bring artillery shells to the gunners from the corps and divisional areas who would have taken delivery from third line units. Until the advent of DROPS each location would have involved manpower and fork-lift operations. Now the loads arrive on flat-racks which can be unloaded complete by the vehicle's integral hydraulic system. The load can remain stored on the flat-rack until required when it is simply lifted back on again. Should the load require splitting at any point it is much easier to handle at ground level. In the meantime the truck can be away on its next task having spent a matter of minutes loading or unloading.

Opposite page, centre: The FH70 is a 155mm field howitzer designed for the general and close support role. An international project, the FH70 was designed and built in Britain, West Germany and Italy as a co-operative effort. It currently serves with these three armies as well as having been exported to others. It is fitted with an Auxiliary Power Unit (APU) and can be seen here in its self-propelled capability although the FH70 is normally towed by a Foden 6x6 Gun Tractor. This can reach speeds of up to 100km/hr on roads. It is fitted with a removable heated cabin for the gun crew and space for four pallets of ammunition which can be lifted or dropped by an integral hydraulic crane. An FH70 Gun Limber variant can carry eight pallets of ammunition and can be fitted with a hydraulic crane. The FH70 is air portable in a Hercules.

Opposite page, bottom: A total of 71 FH70 have been built for the British Army, 216 for the West German and 164 for the Italian Armies. Further examples have been sold to Saudi Arabia and Japan. B Battery, I RHA, was the first unit to receive the FH70 in 1978, and currently three UK-based regiments are equipped with the howitzer. A self-propelled variant designated SP70 reached prototype stage but eventually fell by the wayside and the requirement is being filled by the AS90.

Below: The FH70 fires all NATO 155mm ammunition and has a range of 24 kilometres. This can be extended to 30 kilometres with the use of base bleed shells. Normal firing rate is six rounds per minute although a burst rate of three rounds in thirteen seconds can be achieved. The FH70 is seen here firing in the FIBUA training village on Salisbury Plain.

Below left: A range of ammunition has been developed for the FH70 which includes HE, smoke, base bleed and sub-munition. The ammunition is supplied in two parts – the shell and the propellant. The propellant is supplied in eight bags or charges in the shell case. Depending on the mission some of these bags may be removed to reduce the range.

Below centre: The 155mm sub-munition shell can carry 88 dual-purpose M77 anti-personnel, anti-*matériel* bomblets similar to the 644 carried in an MLRS rocket. At a pre-set height the shell ejects the bomblets to saturate the target.

Below right: These models illustrate the base bleed ammunition (left) and the experimental rocket-assisted ammunition (right). On firing, the base bleed shell ignites the propellant in the base which will extend its range from 24 to 30 kilometres. A rocket-assisted shell is in the process of development which should extend the range even further.

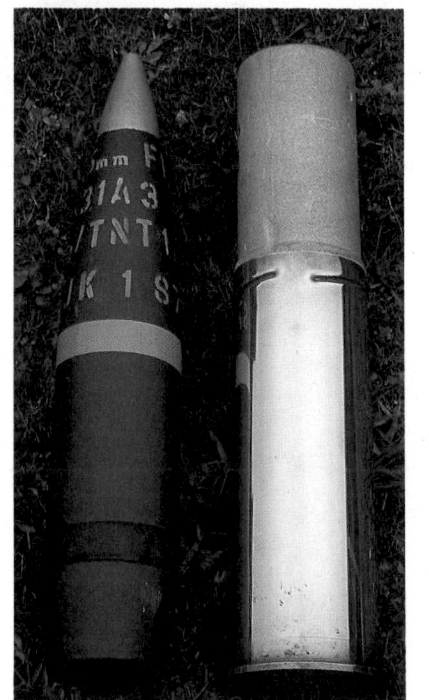

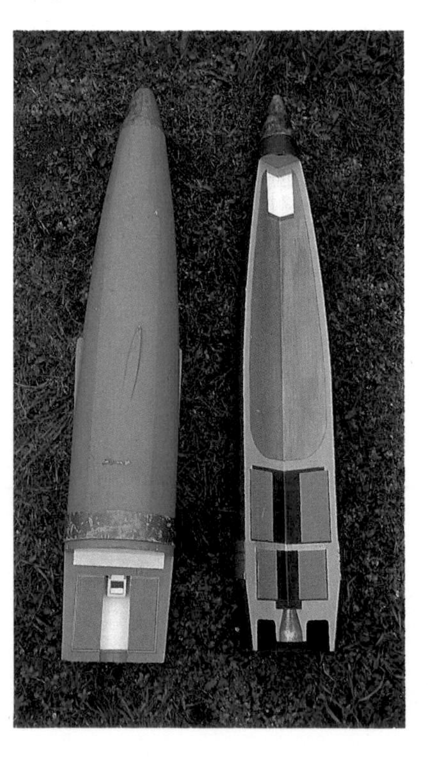

Right: The FV433 Abbot Self-Propelled Gun uses a number of components from the FV432 family of vehicles. The first Abbot was completed in 1961 and production ran from 1964 to 1967. It equips Royal Artillery Regiments both in UK and Germany. In addition, a Value-Engineered Abbot was subsequently produced with export in mind. This simplified version was taken into service by the Indian Army, but four were ordered for Army use on the Suffield Training Ground in Canada.

The FV433 Abbot is powered by a multi-fuel engine and is capable of 48km/hr. It is armed with a 105mm gun plus 7.62mm L4A4 Machine-Gun for self-defence. With the increasing armour protection on modern vehicles it has been assessed that the 105mm blast effect is approximately one-third of that produced by the 155mm. In addition, the Abbot's range of 17 kilometres was no longer sufficiently deep. Thus although originally the Abbot was a reliable vehicle, with an accurate gun, technology was gradually overtaking it.

After twenty-five years' use its reliability has been slipping and its own armour is now classed as lacking. Following tests with the M109 a decision to move ahead with a 155mm howitzer – the Self-Propelled 70 (SP70) – with Italy and Germany. When this was cancelled VSEL was already advanced with a proposal for the export market. Designated AS90, following demonstrations and trials it has been adopted as the Abbot's successor.

Right: Requirements for a new self-propelled howitzer in the USA led to the development of a family of guns using the same chassis. Some of these, the M107 and M110, were purchased by MoD for the British Army. The M107 (at rear) with its 10.87m barrel originally entered service in 1965 and had a maximum range of 32,700 metres, but is now due to be withdrawn. It is being replaced by the MLRS. In front is the M109 (which entered service at the same time) which provides artillery support with its 155mm gun which can fire a 95lb HE shell up to 18,000 metres.

Left: The M109 is an American-designed self-propelled howitzer with a range of 18,000 metres. When it entered service with the British Army in 1965 the M109 became the standard equipment for the Artillery's medium self-propelled batteries. Initially it had the shorter 23.4 calibre barrel which gave it a range of only 14,700 metres, but in the late 1970s these were changed for the longer 39 calibre barrel which gave it the extended range. It was planned that the M109 would be replaced by the SP70. This project has since been cancelled and the AS90 ordered instead. At present it is intended to operate both the M109 and AS90.

Below: The British Army has taken delivery of between six and seven hundred Chieftains of various marks. Most of the older MBTs have now been relegated to training purposes at the RAC School at Bovington. Others have been converted to the AVLB role, the turrets being removed and replaced by bridges.

Right: The Chieftain's 120mm gun is regarded as being one of the most powerful in the world, and thought to be capable of defeating most armour. The effect of the rifled barrel can be seen from the tracer which has scribed a spiral effect as the shell travels down range. The purpose of imparting the spin on the shell is to stabilize it in flight.

Centre right: Both the Chieftain and the Challenger use the L11 tank gun for which they can carry a range of ammunition. The narrow black round is the APFSDS (Armour-Piercing Fin Stabilized Discarding Sabot), the black with a yellow nose is HESH, green is smoke, blue is PRAC SH and the short blue pointed round DS/T PRAC.

The APFSDS is a heavy tungsten dart-like projectile which when fired will discard the plastic three-piece sabot as it leaves the barrel. The kinetic energy stored in the projectile is sufficient to penetrate most armour. The Smoke shell will produce a visually opaque smoke for at least 30 seconds depending on wind strength. The DS/T PRAC is the practice version of the APDS and APFSDS ammunition.

Each of the shells uses a separate bag propellant which burns completely on firing. This reduces fumes from the shell case being brought inside the hull. Additional shells in this family include Illum and APDS.

Bottom right: The Vickers Defence Systems FV4030/4 Challenger is the current generation Main Battle Tank (MBT) for the British Army in Germany. It has been replacing the previous generation Chieftain with an initial order for 240 announced in 1980. The Challenger is fitted with the same main armament as the Chieftain, but these are to be replaced with the new 120mm L30 gun which will also be fitted to the Challenger II. Although based on the Chieftain, Challenger has the new Rolls-Royce 1,200hp engine giving superior performance over the underpowered Chieftain. The application of Chobham armour has also greatly improved its ATGW defences. It has been stated that it is virtually immune to all modern anti-armour projectiles.

Top and above: Replenishing the Challenger's 48 to 64 three-part main rounds can provide good exercise for the crew. The rounds are stowed below the turret ring for extra safety, plus 4,000 rounds of 7.62mm for the L8A2 and L37A2 machine-guns. The three-part main rounds comprise a detonating cartridge, bagged charge and shell. This system does away with the large cartridge-case, and while single shots may take slightly longer to re-load the loader will not be exhausted so quickly in repeated firing as when loading the heavy and awkward one-piece shell.

Right: Despite a weight of 62,000 kilograms the Challenger is capable of a road speed of 56km/h. With its stabilized sight it is able to fire on the move, although not quite so accurately as when stationary, but thanks to its hydrogas suspension it is even better than the already effective Chieftain.

Left: While the DROPS principle has been established for some time, its application and final choice of manufacturer has taken the Ministry of Defence and the politicians some time to conclude. Eventually an order for 1,534 of the Medium Mobility Load Carriers was placed with Leyland DAF. They are being built at their plant at Leyland in Lancashire together with another order for the 4-tonne trucks. The Flatracks are being built by Marshalls of Cambridge.

Left: The Royal Army Ordnance Corps (RAOC) provide a diverse range of functions in support of virtually all aspects of the Army. Besides the holding and issuing of items from its stores, the RAOC has specialist technicians to cover ammunition, photography and EOD amongst others. It is the role of the RAOC to ensure that demands for a diverse range of items are satisfied as quickly as possible. This JCB of 90 Ordnance Company is moving a container of water ready for issue to a unit in the Gulf. It could just as easily be ammunition or a Challenger engine.

Left: The M548 is a US-designed tracked cargo carrier. It is based on the M113 APC family of vehicles and has been purchased for various re-supply roles. In addition, a specialized variant was purchased for re-supplying the Tracked Rapier vehicle for which the M548 is fitted with a crane on the front of the cab.

Right: The Artillery Trainer is used at the School of Artillery to give trainee gunners practical experience in the laying of a gun. The sight used is a standard artillery piece fitted to a miniature gun which fires a 14.5mm round to simulate the shell. The range comprises a number of model buildings and the trainee gunners are given the bearing and ranges of different targets on which to lay the gun.

Below: The 25pdr Gun Howitzer entered service in 1940 and was withdrawn from front-line artillery use in 1967. It was replaced by the 105mm Pack Howitzer and later still by the Light Gun. It has since remained as a ceremonial gun and is also used by a number of OTUs and a few other units. Ammunition is now becoming scarce and supplies may well be obtained from overseas where the 25pdr still remains in front-line service.

Above: The L119 Light Gun is similar to the L118, but the barrel is shorter. The reason is that the L118 requires its own ammunition to obtain its optimum performance. Large stocks of the American M1 ammunition exist but are not compatible with the L118 barrel. As a result a separate barrel has been produced which is shorter and has a different muzzle brake.

Left: The L119 modification is used for training as well as for demontration and trials. The main effect is the reduction in the gun's range from 17,200 metres of the L118 to the 11,400 metres of the L119. It is possible to change the barrels over – the conversion takes approximately two hours.

Above right: The School of Artillery retains a few old 5.5in guns for training as well as demonstration and

trials work because of the large quantity of ammunition still available and for which there is no other use.

Right: The Challenger Trainer Tank (CTT) is a cost-effective training vehicle for Challenger drivers. The gun turret has been replaced by a glass penthouse in which the instructor sits and from which he has a clear panoramic view. In September 1989 Vickers Defence Systems delivered the first of thirty CTTs. They are being used by the Royal Armoured Corps (RAC) at Bovington for driver training and the REME for maintenance and repair crews. Another variant entering service with the British Army is the Challenger ARRV (Armoured Repair and Recovery Vehicle) of which 80 have been ordered. It is capable of towing a 68-tonne tank at 30km/hr.

Above left: Having been selected for aircrew training the student pilot will learn the basics of flying on the Chipmunk primary trainer of the Initial Fixed Wing Flight at the Army Aviation Centre at Middle Wallop.

Above: The Chipmunk has been used in the training role since the AAC became responsible for training its own pilots in 1957. Prior to this the task was carried out by the RAF. Before a pilot can commence training on helicopters he must complete the fixed-wing course and become fully competent in handling and procedures.

Left: Before each flight the instructor briefs the trainee pilot. The briefing is all-important, all aspects of the sortie being discussed including tasks, routing, call signs, radio frequencies, weather, emergencies, serviceability of the aeroplane or helicopter, and procedures.

Army Air Corps

Although the Army had been going aloft since before the First World War (in observation balloons), the Army Air Corps (AAC) was not formed until 1 September 1957, by which time the Auster was the standard aircraft being used for Air Observation Post (AOP) and the liaison roles. In 1958 came the introduction of the AAC's first helicopter – the Skeeter. During the early 1960s these were replaced by the Alouette II and the Scout AH.1. Meanwhile fixed wing operations had acquired the rugged Beaver AL.1. By 1964 the Sioux started to enter service and in 1967 it was decided to give the Scout an anti-tank role. A number were therefore converted to carry the French SS.11 missile. By 1973 the French-designed, Westland-built Gazelle started to enter service to replace the Sioux in the AOP as well as the communications and training roles. Another Westland product – the Lynx – started to replace the Scout from 1978.

The Headquarters of the Army Aviation Centre is at Middle Wallop where virtually all members of the AAC will have spent some time as part of their training. For the AAC soldier this would be basic training followed by specialist training such as signals, transport, refuelling and re-arming helicopters. The REME technician's trade training would be in aviation engineering.

Aircrew are drawn from all arms within the Army – not just from the AAC. Any soldier can apply for pilot training after he has reached the rank of corporal. AAC officers can be Direct Entry, that is, coming from school or university. They will undergo their initial training before going to Middle Wallop for their pilot training. Officers who come from other regiments may apply for a pilot's course and if this is completed successfully will fly with the AAC for three years. At the end of this period he may return to his regiment or transfer to the AAC. The selection for all candidates is extremely rigorous.

The AAC consists of four regiments, three of which are based in Germany. A fifth regiment is currently being formed. Squadrons or flights are located at Belize, Berlin, Brunei, Canada, Cyprus, Hong Kong and UNFICYP.

Right: One of the vital elements of initial flying training on the Chipmunk is blind flying. Here the trainee pilot has his cockpit blanked out so that he cannot see out. He is then fully reliant on his instruments and learns to trust them while carrying out various manoeuvres, so that he will be able to cope with bad weather, poor visibility or night flying.

Left: The Westland Scout was originally designed by Saunders Roe for the Royal Navy as the P.531 which first flew in 1958. A trial batch of Scouts was ordered for the Army Air Corps and by 1962 production aircraft entered service. It has proved to be a versatile helicopter although it is showing its age and has largely been replaced by the Lynx.

Originally designed as a utility helicopter, over the years it has been used in a number of roles ranging from an anti-tank missile launching platform to troop carrier to ambulance.

Below: Originally entering service with the Army in 1978, the Lynx AH.1 has been the subject of numerous upgrades. Besides supplying new airframes, the current programme at Westlands is converting the existing AH.1 to Mk 7 standard. This includes fitting an uprated Rolls-Royce Gem 42 engine, a three-pinion main gearbox and a new tail piece with a reverse direction composite tail rotor for improved control authority in strong cross- and tail-winds. This has

resulted in a much improved performance.

The Lynx provides the Battlegroup Commander with his HELARM capability. Fitted with eight TOW wire-guided missiles, the Lynx would normally be directed by a forward air controller or by the Gazelle AH.1 operating in the air observation post role. Once launched the missile takes 21.5 seconds to reach its maximum effective range of 3,750 metres, but will hit a target at 2,000 metres in just eight seconds.

Above: In the UK the Scout is based at Netheravon with 658 Squadron plus 666 Squadron AAC (Volunteers). Overseas, only 660 Squadron remains equipped with the Scout, based at Sek Kong in Hong Kong with a detachment in Brunei. A few other Scouts are based at Middle Wallop for demonstration and trials as well as conversion flying.

Below: The biannual airshow at the Army Aviation Centre Middle Wallop is the AAC's opportunity to display its skill and capabilities. One of the most impressive and unique items is the mass formation of some forty Scouts, Gazelles and Lynx helicopters from UK and BAOR squadrons.

Left: The latest ACC type is the Pilatus Britten-Norman Islander AL.1 of which seven have been ordered. This has been introduced into Army Air Corps inventory to replace the Beaver AL.1 which has now been retired. Five were initially ordered in 1988. Like its predecessor, the Islander has a STOL (Short Take Off and Landing) capability and will be required to carry out a wide range of roles from liaison and photographic to reconnaissance.

The Islander, which is basically a low-tech airframe, carries some high-tech electronic aids which can be seen from the cockpit instrumentation – a significant factor in the demise of the Beaver was its low electrical power capacity.

Left: Pilots with some 2,000 hours of helicopter flying can convert to the Islander. Many have applied as this will provide them with plenty of Airways and instrument flying experience for when they have completed their service commitment.

A refresher course of 30 hours on the Chipmunk readjusts the pilot from rotary wing to fixed wing techniques, after which he goes to the Advanced Fixed Wing Flight for flying training on the Islander, at AAC Middle Wallop. A total of 90 hours' conversion is flown, of which 50 are in general handling. After this follows a further 32 hours of instrument flying instruction which includes Airways.

Left: One Islander served in the Gulf where it became known as 'Pinky' because of its desert colour scheme. It was used there for four months as a communications aircraft flying senior BFME (British Force Middle East) around the Gulf as required. It is seen here at Al Jubail airfield where it was based. The black and white stripes were painted to aid identification of Allied aircraft. During its deployment it flew more than 600 hours and was serviceable everyday except one when an engine was changed.

Tradition and Ceremonial

The British Army is steeped in the history that has accrued from the many regiments that have formed since the mid 17th Century. The Guards of the Household Division with their bearskins or the Life Guards and Blues and Royal with their white or red plumes represent for many the traditions of the British Army. Many visitors to London think that these soldiers' only duty is to stand guard at Buckingham Palace. In fact they are all regular soldiers with a fighting role within the Army. The Coldstream Guards and units of the Grenadier Guards, Scots Guards and Life Guards all served during the Gulf War.

The 11th Dragoons escorted Prince Albert from Dover to Canterbury. He was impressed with the Squadron and requested that they be known as the 11th Prince Albert's Own Hussars and should wear trousers of the colour of his crimson livery. Over the years this Regiment's name has changed to 11th Hussars and then to The Royal Hussars, but the tradition has remained and as a result they are the only regiment to wear crimson trousers.

The Blues and Royals' blue tunics date back to 1661, being the livery colour of the Earl of Oxford who commanded them when reformed.

Right: Music has always been a major element in the history of the army, from the simple drum used to keep marching men in step, to the regiment's marches and airs played during battle as a morale booster and to identify a regiment's location to its men.

Today music tends to be associated with ceremonial occasions and one such military tradition is now commemorated on Her Majesty The Queen's Birthday Parade. Seen here at the Maifeld, Berlin is the Trooping the Colour of the 1st Battalion The Light Infantry, with music being played by the Massed Bands of the Berlin Infantry Brigade.

Left: The 1st Battalion The Light Infantry originates from the Light Infantry Regiments of the counties of Somerset, Cornwall, Yorkshire, Shropshire, Hereford and Durham.

The Light Infantry were raised originally as a lightly clad, fast moving force. This is reflected in their marching which is at the double. The occasion illustrated is Trooping the Colour to celebrate the Birthday of Her Majesty The Queen, held on the Maifeld in Berlin which is part of the Olympic Stadium.

Trooping the Colour is one of the oldest military ceremonies and goes back to the days when each commander had a regimental standard which, before battle, was paraded through the ranks so that all might see and identify it. During the fighting it would be raised as a rallying point, and at the end of the day's fighting the Colour would be set up where the regimental commander billeted for the night so that stragglers could find their way back to their regiment.

Below: Members of the Massed Bands of the Berlin Brigade prepare to march off at the end of the Queen's Birthday Parade. Besides training as musicians, the bandsmen are trained as medical orderlies and stretcher-bearers which is their wartime role.

Right: The King's Troop RHA provide spectacular entertainment to many thousands of members of the public during ceremonial events and other functions, not only in this country but throughout the world. Each soldier of the Troop must learn to ride and those with most promise are trained to ride on parade or as limber gunners; others work a stablemen.

The men are encouraged to take part individually in shows and competitions and some have had successes in the Olympics. Others work as saddlers, farriers, clerks, tailors, storemen, vehicle drivers or orderlies. Although some knowledge of horses and riding is desirable before joining, a keenness to learn together with a fondness for horses can be sufficient.

Below: The King's Troop Royal Horse Artillery are part of the Household Troop and fire the Royal Salutes in Hyde Park on royal anniversaries and state occasions. The title 'Royal' was conferred by His Majesty King George VI on the Riding Troop in 1947, it being his wish that a mounted and traditionally dressed Troop should once more grace state occasions. Her Majesty has retained the title in accordance with her father's wish.

Below: The officers and men of the Grenadier Guards line the route for a state visit. The First or Grenadier Regiment of Foot Guards, which was usually shortened to Grenadier Guards, was the first of the Guards regiments to wear the bearskin, in the early 1800s. The regiment has taken part in almost every major campaign since Tangier in 1680 and provided a Headquarters plus two Companies for the Gulf War.

Left: Although perceived as purely ceremonial guards by most international visitors, the Blues and Royals have alternated their roles with the Life Guards and spend half their time operationally in Germany equipped with the Challenger as part of the Army's NATO force.

Centre left: The ceremonial duties are carried out by both regiments, who supply a detachment of squadron strength. Together these comprise the Household Cavalry Mounted Regiment and are stationed in London. It is this regiment that provides the mounted and dismounted men who carry out the traditional ceremonial duties of the Household Cavalry – The Queen's Life Guard at Horse Guards, Whitehall and the dismounted detachment who line processional routes. In addition they provide the Sovereign's Escort to Her Majesty The Queen whenever she travels by carriage. Seen here is the Sovereign's Escort riding past Windsor Castle on the occasion of the State Visit of the President of Poland.

Bottom left: The Blues and Royals was formed in 1969 from the amalgamated Royal Horse Guards (The Blues) and the Royal Dragoons (1st Dragoons). The Royal Horse Guards were directly descended from the Regiment of Horse raised by Cromwell in 1650. The Royal Dragoons (1st Dragoons) were, until the amalgamation, the oldest cavalry regiment of the line, having been raised in 1661 as The Tangier Horse. Having spent 22 years fighting the Moors, it received the title His Majesty's Own Royal Regiment of Dragoons. The term 'dragoon' was derived from the 'dragon' which was a 16th-Century musket suitable for mounted infantry.

Left: Colonel-in-Chief The Royal Hussars (Prince of Wales's Own), HRH Princess Alice Duchess of Gloucester presenting the new guidon to the Regiment. The guidon is the Light Cavalry's equivalent of the Infantry's Colour. The colour, or standard as it was originally called, evolved from the banners carried by the knights of the Middle Ages.

British Army of the Rhine

The primary role of NATO, of which the British Army is part, is the defence of western Europe which it does in co-operation with our allies. At the end of the Second World War the Russians ceased to work in conjunction with the Allies with the result that British, French and US troops remained in Germany, initially as a force of occupation, and then as a protective force for West Germany.

Meanwhile in East Germany the Soviet troops remained in far greater strength. During the 1980s these included twenty-six Soviet Divisions plus ten Czech, fifteen Polish and six DDR. Together with reinforcements there were about ninety divisions facing NATO.

To counter this threat Germany was split into three defence regions for each of which one of the Allies would be primarily responsible. Britain has been responsible for a 65-kilometre stretch of the Central Front and has recently had 56,000 troops in Germany to make up the British Army of the Rhine (BAOR). In time of tension or war 1 (BR) Corps would provide the defensive force consisting of 1st and 3rd Armoured Divisions, each with three armoured brigades plus 4th Armoured Division with two brigades. In addition an artillery brigade would provide air defence throughout the corps area and provide depth fire support.

Numbers would be greatly boosted by reinforcements from the UK in the form of Regular, TA and Reservists, bringing total strength up to approximately 130,000. The regular 19 Brigade would deploy from the UK to complete 4th Armoured Division. 2nd Infantry Division in the form of two TA infantry brigades plus 24 Airmobile Brigade would make up the deployed reserve. If required, 50 Missile Regiment would provide 1 (BR) Corps with a theatre nuclear capability with its Lance missiles. To support 1 (BR) Corps is the British Rear Combat Zone, based at Düsseldorf, with logistic support and behind that the British Communications Zone centred at Emblem in Belgium. This provides the points of entry for reinforcement units and supplies from the UK.

There has been a certain amount of tension in Germany ever since the Second World War and it was probably at its height during the blockade of Berlin in 1948-9 when all road and rail access was blocked by the Soviets. They thought that this would starve the defenders of Berlin out and result in complete Soviet occupation of Berlin. The Allies mounted a massive airlift which flew in all the foodstuffs, fuel and other necessities to keep the city going.

To enable 1 (BR) Corps to be fully prepared for any possible conflict, exercises are held on a regular basis both on and off the training ground. These can be purely by the British Army or in conjunction with other members of NATO. Traditionally the off training area exercises take place in the autumn before the planting of the winter crops.

During the last few years the easing of tension in Germany has led to various agreements for the destruction of large quantities of nuclear weapons. These have progressed even further to the limiting of numbers of armoured fighting vehicles. As a result the scale of exercises have reduced to the extent that some are purely for command and control with Land Rovers simulating squadrons of tanks and APCs. Following the reunification of East and West Germany they are being reduced further and the recent break up of the Soviet Union will see even fewer of these exercises.

Left: The British Army is rapidly replacing the 7.62mm SLR and the 9mm SMG with the SA80 family of small calibre weapon. These are magazine fed and gas-operated weapons and can fire single rounds or automatic bursts.

Centre left: Milan is considered to be an effective anti-tank weapon, but along with the 66mm HEAT and 94mm LAW when a well-defended enemy position is holding up an attack and inflicting casualties, Milan could be the answer. Although expensive it may be the cheapest answer in terms of lives saved, but such weapons cannot be used extravagantly. Events during the heat of the battle will dictate the best use of the weapons available.

Bottom left: The infantry served in the Gulf in considerable numbers, six battalions being deployed. These men took part in the build-up exercises that provided refresher training for desert warfare which had not been practised regularly on such a scale by the British Army for many years.

Top right: One of the infantrymen deployed to the Gulf mans his GPMG at his prepared defensive position. He awaits any sign of an Iraqi attack. During the build-up of Allied forces a series of exercises prepared the men for desert fighting which required different tactics from the normal training in Germany where natural cover and landmarks are abundant.

Bottom right: The Land Rover has been the general workhorse light vehicle for the British Army since the mid 1950s. Originally evolved as an industrial/agricultural vehicle, the success of the Land Rover series of vehicles is such that it has been sold to virtually every country in the world in either its civilian or military guise and more than 1.7 million have been built.

Over the years it has developed from the ¼-ton to the ½-tonne and ¾-tonne. Recent developments include the Land Rover 90 and 110 variants of which some 2,500 have been ordered for the army recently. Some 25,000-30,000 vehicles have been built for the British Army.

200 RDS
MXD LNK
7.62mm
IN
MK 1
L2A2
71 KF 26

Left: An FV432 emerges from woods and moves around the edge of a farmer's field in Germany. This vehicle is fitted with the GPMG turret and is part of the simulated enemy 'Orange' forces signified by the orange tape.

Centre left: The M548 was used in the Gulf to carry munitions for the various guns. Being tracked, the M548 has more of a 'go anywhere' capability than wheeled vehicles although soft sand was not too much of a problem during the conflict. This vehicle belonged to the Staffordshire Regiment.

Bottom left: Despite being replaced by the Warrior, the FV432 saw service in the Gulf. This example served in support of the Staffords.

Opposite page, top: The FV432 can easily be converted to the ambulance role by removing all the armaments other than smoke-dischargers. Capacity exists in the FV432 to fit four stretchers on racks or five sitting casualties with two stretchers.

Opposite page, bottom: In Germany each of the armoured reconnaissance regiments of 1 (BR) Corps has one squadron of the FV107 Scimitar and these could be deployed in direct support of infantry combat teams or battle groups. In the UK the medium reconnaissance troop would use a mix of Scorpion and Scimitar. The Scimitars, such as this example with the 16th/5th The Queen's Royal Lancers, were deployed to the Gulf and were operating anything up to 70 miles in front of the Allies' front line.

10
35 KG 12

Opposite page, top: A Striker prepares for possible action while stopped in a German village on exercise. If necessary the Striker can be operated while parked, out of sight of the enemy, the layer being located elsewhere, possibly up to 100 metres away, with a clear view of the targets.

Opposite page, bottom: The Warrior Section vehicle has a crew of three: commander, driver and gunner, and it can carry seven fully equipped troops. It has greater armour protection than the FV432 which it is replacing. It has better manoeuvrability and firepower which consists of a 30mm Rarden Gun and a 7.62mm Chain Gun on its turret, with stowage provided in the hull for eight 94mm LAW. The Raven Image Intensification Sight enables target acquisition at night up to 1,000 metres.

The Warrior is seen as the main infantry support vehicle and an initial order for 1,048 vehicles was placed and deliveries are due to be completed in 1994.

Top right: The Warrior APC has sufficient supplies for the crew of three plus seven fully armed troops to enable them to remain on the battlefield for 48 hours in NBC conditions. To give cover for troops deploying in open country or while withdrawing, the multi-barrel smoke-dischargers can discharge white phosphorous grenades which produce an instant wall of thick white smoke. Similar mountings are fitted to most assault, reconnaissance and armoured vehicles.

Right: The wearing of NBC clothing has become a fact of life for the serviceman and would be a great lifesaver should such an attack occur. While the British NBC suit and the S10 respirator are better than many others in that some air circulation is given around the body, there can be no getting away from the fact that they are uncomfortable and will reduce the efficiency of the soldier. Any vigorous movement can cause a build-up of moisture, and in cold weather the condensation could cause problems. Communication is also restricted, but without this protection injuries would be horrendous if not fatal.

Above: The up-armoured Warrior of the 1st Battalion, The Staffordshire Regiment (The Prince of Wales's Own), which was part of 7 Armoured Brigade, proved to be a very important ingredient in the Gulf. According to Brigadier Cordingley, during a 68-hour period they advanced more than 300 kilometres and fought a number of battles. During this time the 155 Warriors that made up 4 Armoured Brigade were never more than two down on their strength.

Left: While helicopters can move troops over short distances, the Hercules is the RAF's main means of moving troops quickly over moderate distances. It is capable of operating from semi-prepared airstrips such as this one in the Gulf and can seat up to 92 men.

Opposite page, top, left and right: The commander and gun loader sit in the turret of their Chieftain, parked on the edge of a wooded area, and keep watch for the advancing enemy. Mounted on the commander's cupola is a 7.62mm machine-gun. Around him can be seen a number of periscopes to assist him when shut down.

Opposite page, bottom: Chieftain of the enemy 'Orange' forces, marked with orange tape, moves off from cover in woods down the edge of a field during a training exercise. The ground is dry and the minimal damage to the field is being confined to the edge.

GASTHAUS Zur Linde

Left: Chieftain MBT takes on fuel from a Stalwart fitted with the bulk fuel dispensing unit while under cover in woodlands. The Chieftain has a range of 200-300 kilometres cross-country and 400-500 kilometres on roads. On recent exercises the strapping of a pair of 50-gallon oil drums on the back of the tank had been successfully experimented with to reduce the refuelling requirements of the MBT, and this extended the range of the Challengers in the Gulf.

Opposite page, bottom: As with the Chieftain, the Challenger gun is fitted with Insumat gun barrel insulation. This can significantly reduce the error to gunsight relationship caused by differential heating or cooling from solar or ground radiation, wind, rain or even firing. It also reduces the infra-red signature of the gun barrel.

Above: Despite some poor previous competition results, the Challenger was highly successful in the Gulf War and surprised many of its critics. During the conflict some 180 of them were manned by the Royal Scots Dragoon Guards (Carabiners and Greys), The Queen's Royal Irish Hussars from 7 Brigade and the 14th/20th King's Hussars of 4 Brigade.

The 59 Challengers of the 14th/20th maintained a minimum of 94 per cent of their tanks on the road, and at the end of the series of battles during the 350-kilometre advance, 53 were still on the road. A total of 420 Challengers were built for BAOR and many of these will be undergoing a substantial upgrade which will include the fitting of a new, more powerful gun.

Below: M110A2 in the Gulf where they were used to fire heavy barrages against Iraqi troops, guns and tanks. This Self Propelled Howitzer is similar in design to the M107 but with an 8in barrel instead of the 175mm. It has a range of 24 kilometres and so would be fired from well behind the front line. As a result it was felt that the chances of it being hit was remote so it has no protective armour for the crew. Such is the size of the shell that only two can be carried on the M110. The M548 is being used here to carry the ammunition.

These M110s from 32nd Heavy Regiment, RA, were in fact M107s which had exchanged their barrels for the 8in, a task which takes about two hours. After their deployment to the Gulf they returned to Germany where they reverted to M107s. Once the MLRS has been delivered all the M107s will be scrapped. It is hoped that the remaining M110s will be sold.

Above: Lance is a ballistic artillery rocket with a range of from 5 to 121 kilometres. Design in the USA commenced in 1962 and it was introduced into the British Army to replace the Honest John. It can be fitted with a conventional or nuclear warhead, but the British Army Lance is only fitted with nuclear weapons, it is considered too expensive to be used as a conventional weapon. It is the standard NATO battlefield support missile system, having been supplied to Belgium, Germany, Italy and the Netherlands. It is seen here being towed while mounted on the lightweight trailer launcher.

Bottom left: 50 Missile Regiment, an element of HQ 1 (BR) Corps, is the only British Army Lance regiment. The missile is normally fired from the tracked M752 Self-Propelled Launcher which is supported by the M688 Loader-Transporter. Both vehicles are based on the M113 family. The M752 SPL is manned by a crew of six who prepare the missile; target details are fed into the missile inertial guidance which controls the missile in flight. Once fired the ground crew have no further control on the missile and it therefore cannot be jammed. The M668 LT has a crew of two and can carry two missiles with their fins removed. It has a small crane to transfer the missiles to the M752.

Bottom right: This Lance on the lightweight trailer-launcher was launched by 15 Missile Battery, RA. On firing, stabilizing jets near the top of the missile eject gases to produce a spinning motion. The main boost motor burns for a period of 1.5–6 seconds depending on the required range.

Right: Multiple Launch Rocket System (MLRS) of 176 (Abu Klea) Battery RA in a German village during a winter exercise. MLRS is a US-designed rocket launcher system which is in production in Europe for the German, Italian, French and British Armies. Fitted with two six-rocket packs, the MLRS can fire each rocket individually or in a ripple of two to twelve in less than one minute.

The 4m-long rocket has solid fuel propulsion and a range of more than 30 kilometres. The advanced fire control system enables the ripple to be fired at single or multiple targets. Having fired, the vehicle can move quickly to another location to avoid return fire and will be ready to fire all remaining rockets within four minutes.

Deliveries are currently continuing of the 63 launchers ordered. When deliveries are complete the UK will have six batteries each with nine launchers. The MLRS is normally manned by a crew of three although in an emergency all the operations including reloading can be carried out by one man.

Right: Each MLRS rocket contains 644 bomblets which can penetrate light armour. Such is the speed of the MLRS that it can devastate an area of one square kilometre (six football pitches) and move on before an enemy can return fire. A salvo of twelve rockets from a single MLRS can place 7,728 M77 bomblets on the target in less than a minute. Conventional artillery such as the 155mm M109 would require 22 guns each to fire four rounds within the minute.

According to the 1991 Defence White Paper the two batteries of MLRS from 39 Heavy Regiment, RA were described as a 'battle winner'. The Iraqis described the showers of bomblets as 'black rain'. An Iraqi artillery commander was reported as saying that 90 per cent of his crews on his position had been killed during one bombardment and, including the follow-up, more than 70 guns were lost in just one hour.

Eventually the British Army will be receiving the Phase III version of MLRS ammunition which will have a Terminal Guidance Warhead (TGW). The submunitions will include three anti-armour submissiles which can seek, track and home in on tanks and heavy armour.

Left: The Tracked Rapier is based on the fitting of the missile system on to a variant of the M113 APC. An order was received from the Iranians but was halted at an advanced stage with the toppling of the Shah. The British Army trials on the system resulted in an order for fifty and then for an additional twenty.

The Tracked Rapier has a crew of three accommodated within an armoured cab. The advantage over the towed Rapier is that it is capable of being ready for action within fifteen seconds of stopping whereas the towed system can take thirty minutes, making it far more mobile and effective than the towed system.

Left: The Rapier is a light-weight missile weighing only 43 kilograms and eight can be fitted on the Tracked Rapier. It has a high degree of manoeuvrability which gives it an impressive performance against high-speed crossing targets. The performance of the Rapier missile is such that it operated as a 'hittile' with a semi-armoured piercing warhead.

Left: The Rapier fire control has been improved with introduction of the Field Standard B2 (FSB2) Rapier 'Darkfire' system. This includes a new electro-optical tracker which enables targets to be engaged by day and by night. It also permits tracking in light mist, smoke and dust. Work is progressing on the next generation Field Standard C and development of the Mk II missile has been completed.

Right: For practice firing of the Rapier missiles the Army uses the Rushton Target which is an air-to-air missile-sized system towed by the RAF Hawk T.1 of 100 Squadron on a long cable. It contains a miss-distance indicator which allows the operators' performance to be determined. Being a towed system the Rushton Target has little manoeuvrability and its training effectiveness while valuable has a limited effect.

A more expensive but more realistic target system is the Flight Refuelling ASAT (Advanced Subsonic Aerial Target), known as Falconet, in service with the British Army. The Falconet is used on the RA ranges at Benbecula in the Hebrides and resembles a small, fast and manoeuvrable, fighter-like target for training and live firing. As with the Rushton Target the Falconet is fitted with a miss-distance indicator which is important because a near-miss on this target might be significant, the target being smaller than an aircraft. The ASAT is also used by the French in a similar role.

Right: 12 Air Defence Regiment with Rapier was deployed to the Gulf to protect key installations, but the absence of Iraqi intruding aircraft meant that no missiles were fired. Although the Rapier system can be operated using the optical fire unit to counter the threat of anti-radar missiles, the Blindfire radar can produce an automatic, 24-hour, all-weather target- and missile-tracking capability.

Right: Depending on the nature of the threat and the conditions, Rapier can be used in the automatic or the manual mode or a combination of both. During the Gulf build-up and in the early days of the conflict the threat was high, but as events proceeded attacks were desultory. The defences were maintained at a high state of readiness however.

Left: The Shorts Javelin is an advanced development of the Blowpipe close air-defence missile which entered service in 1975 and saw service during the Falklands Campaign. It uses a Semi-Automatic Command to Line Of Sight (SACLOS) guidance system which consists of a stabilized tracking and auto-guidance system. This requires the operator to track the target throughout the engagement and the system will compensate for cross-winds and automatically generates a lead-angle to steer the missile ahead of the crossing targets. The man-portable Javelin enables the operator to react quickly to any attacking aircraft or helicopter and achieve a high kill rate.

A triple Javelin missile Light Multiple Launcher (LML) is also currently in service. This enables the operator to cope with a number of targets in quick succession without the need to reload.

Left: During the Gulf War Royal Artillery Javelin teams were deployed aboard Royal Navy ships to provide additional air defence cover. Although the Javelin can be operated by a single person it is normally manned by a crew of two, the operator aiming, firing and tracking the missile while the second member fetches reloads, assists with the loading and keeps an eye out for enemy aircraft.

Right: As a result of experiences during the Falklands Campaign it was found that small-arms fire, especially tracer, can have an off-putting effect on attacking pilots. As a result a considerable amount of small-arms AA training is now carried out using a radio-controlled model aircraft, known as MATS-B, at ranges of 500–600 metres which represents an aircraft flying at 400–500 knots.

Right: Apart from its APC role, the large interior capacity of the Saxon has made it useful as a command, ambulance or air-defence vehicle. This Saxon is operated by 53 (Louisburg) Air Defence Battery from 22 Air Defence Regiment and can be fitted with a cupola; a DISA mounted machine-gun is fitted for the air-defence role.

The armour protection provided by Saxon is at least comparable to many tracked armoured vehicles if not better. It gives crew protection against 5.56mm and 7.62 ball and armoured-piercing ammunition, anti-tank mines up to 9 kilograms and 155mm HE airburst fire. A total of 644 Saxons have been ordered for British Army use of which twenty are command posts for the Rapier – the rest are mainly for the infantry battalions.

Right: The Midge is the Canadian AN/USD-501 reconnaissance drone which when launched follows a pre-programmed course and takes photographs at pre-set intervals as well as activating its infra-red sensors. It has a range in excess of 150 kilometres and is normally flown in a circular route so as to return to the launch site where the film is processed and interpreted. Dried negatives can be made available within approximately one hour of the information being requested. Midge will be replaced shortly by Phoenix which is able to transmit images back 'live' and can have its route changed from that planned during the flight should an interesting target be seen.

Left: DROPS provided an invaluable tool to the RCT tasked with re-supply in the Gulf War. Sixty of these vehicles were allocated to 12 Squadron RCT which was tasked with moving ammunition, fuel and water. As the DROPS concept was still in its early days the squadron not only had to adjust to the desert conditions but evolve a new code of operations. Once up and running the squadron moved in one month two million litres of water, 100 ISO containers plus the more than 7,000 tons of ammunition for which the system was originally intended.

Left: The Stalwart is a high mobility load carrier which has an amphibious capability. Its go virtually anywhere ability makes it an ideal replenishment vehicle. It is seen here fitted with the bulk fuel dispensing unit which comprises two 2,100-litre fuel tanks with a pumping and dispensing pack. It can offload fuel at the rate of 455 litres per minute.

Left: An Aardvark demonstrating its front-mounted flail. As the vehicle, whose driver is well protected, passes through a minefield the flail churns and pounds the ground, smashing or detonating any mine encountered.

Right: A number of the Aardvark mine-clearance vehicles were purchased by the army and flown out by civilian air charter for use in the Gulf where they were operated by the sappers of the Flail Troop, 32 Armoured Engineer Regiment.

Right: A mineplough can be fitted to the front of the Challenger or Chieftain MBTs or, in this case, the Centurion AVRE. The plough can clear parallel tracks of ground, $1\frac{1}{2}$ metres wide and 200–300mm deep, from in front of the tank, the soil (and any anti-tank or personnel mines) being pushed out to each side. When used by the Royal Engineers the Chieftain and Centurion AVRE are likely to use the Pathfinder marker system as seen here. This fires a series of rods to mark the cleared path, or can be used to indicate areas of contamination or approach areas. At the rear is the Giant Viper minefield breaching system which would probably be used if speed were essential or if the ground were unsuitable for the plough.

Above: An FV432 from the RA ranges at Lulworth Cove tows the Giant Viper trailer to the range for a demonstrating firing. Although the rocket is live the charge is inert. Such is the destructive power of the Giant Viper that the full system is only fired at BATUS.

Below left: When the Giant Viper is required to be deployed eight rocket charges are fitted into the projector which is located on an angled aiming post at the back of the trailer.

Below right: The Giant Viper, designed to clear any type of minefield, but primarily anti-tank minefields, consists of a trailer in which is stowed a 229-metre hose packed with plastic explosives. The trailer is towed to within 45 metres of the edge of the suspected minefield by a Centurion AVRE, FV180 CET or an FV432. A cluster of eight rockets is aligned to the path required and is fired from the AVRE. The rockets are stabilized in flight by three parachutes and unfurl the hose. Once on the ground, the explosive contents of the hose is detonated from within the towing vehicle. The path cleared is up to 7.28 metres wide and up to 189 metres long. Another Viper is brought up and the process is repeated until the minefield has been crossed.

Right: One of the specialist roles of the RE (Royal Engineers) and RAOC is that of EOD (Explosive Ordnance Disposal). This role is shared with the RAF and the Royal Navy who deal with their own property. The RN handles explosives below the high-water mark. The split between the RE and RAOC is that the RE tends to deal with Second World War bombs, while the RAOC deals with terrorist devices and unwanted or time-expired explosives. In practice, for various reasons, the split is not as clean cut.

Right: The American M18A1 Claymore is a highly lethal anti-personnel mine. Perched on legs, it is normally positioned to cover an expected route and hidden in undergrowth. It is fired by a trip-wire or remotely, and on detonation projects 700 small steel balls some 50 yards. The Claymore is currently being augmented and will eventually be replaced by the Padmine which is similar but its spread of fire is more accurate and it has a range of up to 160 metres.

Right: The French-designed Horizontal Action Anti-tank Mine or Off Route Mine can be used to close roads and gaps in minefields to MBTs and AFVs. When deployed it is anchored to the ground and pointed in the direction the tank is expected to traverse and then camouflaged. A trip-wire is stretched out in line with the mine. When disrupted a shaped charge is fired which can penetrate 50mm of armour at 80 metres' range. Its effectiveness is dependent on the range and angle of impact so its ideal positioning requires careful consideration. A training version is available which fires a marking sponge at the target vehicle.

Left: The Ranger anti-personnel mines (left) are supplied in tubes of eighteen ready for loading on to the projector. The mine, which is a disc 62mm across, is ejected and arms itself twenty seconds later. It contains a 10g charge of RDX/Wax which is of a size aimed to disable rather than kill. It is detonated by touch. It is probable that the Ranger would be used in conjunction with the Bar Mine to provide a comprehensive area denial package. The C3A1 Elsie (right) is a manually laid anti-personnel mine.

Left: The C3A1 Elsie is a Canadian-designed anti-personnel mine which is small and, having no metal parts, is difficult to detect. It requires placing by hand, being pressed into a soft surface, which is assisted by its cone-shaped end, until only the olive-coloured top is visible. It requires a pressure of between 7.25 and 11.8 kilograms to trigger the small charge which, like the Ranger mine, is designed to disable rather than kill. A practice mine designated C4A1 which emits smoke when activated is used as is an inert version for training.

Left: The Anti-Tank Mine Mk 7 remains in service but it is being superseded by the Bar Mine. It requires laying by the traditional manual method. It also contains metal parts and so will have a limited use in the future.

Right: The Bar Mine Layer is normally towed behind an FV432 with the crew under cover although other vehicles can be used. As the vehicle progresses the layer cuts a furrow, the bar mine is placed on the conveyor and the fuze is activated automatically prior to being dropped into the furrow. Then the two disc wheels fill the furrow and smooth the ground surface. A total of 600–700 mines per hour can be laid by one three-man crew vehicle, if sufficient logistic support is provided.

The Bar Mine offers more chance of being activated because of its length. It is intended to attack relatively light belly armour, and can kill an MBT.

Right: Besides ensuring the mobility of friendly forces, one of the many tasks of the Royal Engineers is to provide obstacles against an advancing enemy. These can be earthworks in the form of ditches and tank-traps constructed with the aid of the CET. A Rapid Cratering Kit will produce a crater 6m wide by 2m deep from 20 kilograms of explosives in just ten minutes – highly effective in blocking roads.

Blowing bridges is another effective slowing factor. With the explosives in position the commander has two options: to blow the bridge immediately, which will lose the element of surprise and give the enemy time to make an alternative plan, or he can wait until the enemy approaches and then blow it. While this would cause a major disruption it also runs the risk that an advanced party of enemy engineers may inspect the bridge un-noticed and defuze the explosives.

Above: If a cavalry or infantry vehicle breaks down, the REME (Royal Electrical and Mechanical Engineers) attached to the unit, will have an LAD (Light Air Detachment) which will undertake small repairs. Any major tasks will require the vehicle to be removed to the field workshop.

Above right: Any breakdown during an exercise will produce urgent activity to put it right. Here a repair to a Chieftain's main drive requires the track to be removed and welding to be carried out. On exercises the REME are required not only to carry a range of spares but also a variety of kit to enable them to be able to handle all types of problems in the field.

Below: The FV434 is the Carrier, Maintenance, Full Tracked version of the FV432 family of APC vehicles. It is used by the Royal Electrical and Mechanical Engineers (REME). Its primary role is to repair disabled and damaged vehicles, but it does have a recovery capability. An HIAB crane is fitted to the right side of the vehicle. This has a lifting capability of between 1,250 and 3,050 kilograms depending on the extended radii of the arm. Inside, a full range of tools is stowed as well as a work-bench, vice and towing bars.

Right: The Warrior was deployed to the Gulf in substantial numbers (more than 300) where it was up-armoured for extra protection. In addition to the Warrior Infantry Section Vehicle some of the other variants were deployed. These included the REME Warrior ARV recovery vehicle (illustrated) which has a 6.5-tonne crane plus a twin capstan winch, capable of a pull of up to 38 tonnes.

Other members of the family include Artillery Observation Post (OPV), Battery Commander (BCV) and Infantry Command vehicles. The Warrior OPV is the most complex variant yet, fitted with thermal sights, laser viewfinder plus navigation and target acquisition systems. The role of the Warrior OPV is to detect enemy vehicles and positions and relay the information back to the Artillery Batteries. The BCV will contain a BATES (Battlefield Artillery Target Engagement System) cell.

Below: The FV180 CET (Combat Engineer Tractor) began life as a design at the Military Engineering Experimental Establishment at Christchurch. This was to be an international collaboration project with France and Germany, but they dropped out at an early stage. The CET was designed for a wide range of roles which include bulldozer, tracklayer, preparing crossings, digging defensive positions and towing trailers including Giant Viper.

The CET has a crew of two, a driver and operator, both having reversible seats enabling either to operate the vehicle. It has an amphibious capability with Dowty water jets at the rear. A rocket-powered earth anchor can be used if in difficulty exiting a river or any other obstacle. When deployed operationally it will have fascines strapped to its sides. These consist of black pipes which can be dropped into ditches allowing all kinds of tracked vehicle to cross.

91 ET 34

Opposite page, top: If the REME LAD are unable to make the repair, the disabled vehicle will be recovered to the field workshops. The REME has a variety of recovery vehicles at its disposal. Here they are using the Foden 6x6 to recover a Striker. The Foden has a crane with a maximum lift of 12,500 kilograms and a 25-tonne winch, and has a good cross-country capability.

Opposite page, bottom: The Ferret Scout Car soldiers on, with uses being nearly as diverse as the units with which it serves. It is seen here as part of an REME exercise support team together with the FV624 Stalwart repair vehicle.

Above: The M2 is a German-designed and built amphibious bridging and ferry system. It can be used in two ways: as a ferry – vehicles are driven on to the M2 and then ferried across the water, or as a bridge in which case the required number of M2s are bolted together. The M2 is completely road mobile on four wheels which are raised when floating.

The Army has one M2 regiment – 28 Amphibious Engineer Regiment – made up of two squadrons each equipped with thirty M2s. Each squadron has two troops each with fifteen units plus four which are not manned in peacetime. An improved M3 variant has been the subject of trials and is expected to enter service in the mid 1990s.

Right: To make a ferry platform a number of M2s are coupled together according to the size and weight of the vehicles to be carried, which can include the Challenger. Alternatively the required number of M2s can be coupled together to form a complete bridge. In the water the main engines power two side propellers and an additional engine provides further steering power each of which require a helmsman.

Below: A substantial number of older Chieftain MBTs are being modified to become the FV4205 Chieftain AVLB (Armoured Vehicle Launched Bridge). Used to provide a quick means of crossing a moderate sized obstacle, they have had their turret removed and replaced with either the No.8 Tank Bridge, which can carry vehicles up to Military Load Class 70 (MLC70) over 22.8m gaps, or the No.9 Tank Bridge which spans 12.2 metres.

When travelling the No.8 bridge is stowed on top of the Chieftain, folded in half. To launch the No.9 bridge it is simply rotated through 180 degrees. Depending on the width of the gap to be crossed, the bridges can be used individually or together. The Chieftain AVLB can be fitted with mounting points for the Track Width Mine Plough System. It has a crew of three: commander, radio operator and driver.

The AVLBs here are being escorted by an RE Samson.

Left: To deploy the No.8 bridge it is tilted hydraulically forward over the top of the Chieftain while still folded. Once at the vertical the two sections open out from the hinge at the top. As the two halves open out the whole bridge is lowered until the far end touches the other side of the obstruction. Once this operation is complete the rods can be released, the Chieftain can be driven away and the bridge is ready for use. The launching of the No.8 bridge takes some 3 to 5 minutes and recovery approximately 10 minutes.

Left: Scimitars crossing an MGB (Medium Girder Bridge) spanning a simulated obstacle. The MGB has been highly successful, with overseas sales to numerous countries including the USA. It entered service with the Army in 1971 and has been designed to be easily assembled by hand on an unprepared site with only the heaviest component requiring a six-man lift. A single 9m MGB can be constructed from two pallets of components, while a 31m double-storey bridge capable of supporting a Class 60 vehicle requires ten pallet loads. A reinforcement component can be used to extend the capability of the MGB to 49.4 metres without any loss in weight-carrying capacity. Should this still be too short, a combination of span junctions for use with any form of support or portable pier set is available. The MGB can also be floated and used as a ferry.

Right: The FV105 Sultan provides the Army with an armoured command post which has a standard fit of radio and map boards. Although similar in size and shape to the Samaritan armoured ambulance, due to its role it will be bristling with aerials. Some of the Sultans will eventually be replaced by the Warrior BCV (Battery Command Vehicle) variant.

Below: The Gazelle was designed by Aérospatiale of France as a replacement for the Alouette II of which the British Army had a small number. It was ordered for British use as a replacement for the Sioux AH.1. Built by Westlands under an Anglo/French package which included the Lynx, some 200 Gazelle AH.1s fulfil a range of roles from communications to air observation.

To assist the crew in the observation role the Gazelle AH.1 is fitted with a stabilized sight mounted on the top of the cab. The Gazelle is not normally armed, but this helicopter from 666 Squadron has a pylon fitted to which a machine-gun pod can be attached. During the Falklands Campaign SNEB rocket pods were also fitted.

Left: HELARM is an effective and highly mobile anti-tank reserve which is normally controlled by the Divisional Commander. Where possible the fire positions and killing areas will have been pre-recced by the Gazelle observer and it would be normal for a whole squadron of Lynx to be deployed for any one task. As with all Army operations a clear briefing is essential to provide the latest Intelligence and met reports, objectives, alternatives and command structure to ensure that the objective is achieved as efficiently as possible.

Below: The AAC commitment to BAOR is three regiments: Nos 1, 3 and 4 Regiments plus 664 Squadron plus a Corps flight for VIPs. A total of 113 Lynx AH.1s have been ordered for the Army most of which will be converted to AH.7 standard. In addition, an order for AH.5s has resulted in four being completed and the rest completed as AH.7. A total of eleven new AH.7s have been built and a further order for sixteen Mk 9s is under way. A further eight AH.7s (some of which may be the converted AH.1) are to be converted to Mk 9, all of which are for 24 AMB.

Right: The FARP (Forward Aiming Refuelling Point) team move off to their next location. The FARP are vital to the Lynx and Gazelle operating in the battle area, keeping them armed and providing fuel as required. In battle the squadron base would, of necessity, be some distance from the front line to ensure that its assets were not too vulnerable. The length of transit and therefore the reaction time might be unacceptable. To resolve this a specialist team known as the FARP would deploy to forward areas, provide the necessary fuel and ammunition and move to another position.

Right: Flying out of Kuwait International Airport soon after the conclusion of hostilities is one of 4 Brigade's Gazelle AH.1s. The scene is one of complete devastation, most buildings having been ransacked and then destroyed. Some of the hazards of the war did not manifest themselves immediately; a number of explosive booby-traps were discovered only a hundred metres from this location which had been in constant use by helicopters since the arrival of the Allied forces.

Right: A Gazelle AH.1 of 654 Squadron overflies Iraqi dummy positions made from water tanks with a pole sticking out. When seen from a dug-out or just over the top of a dune, they gave the Allied troops food for thought as there was always the possibility that there was a real gun at that location. As a result extra effort had to be expended in attacking these positions.

Left: During the Gulf War camouflage had a dual purpose. Primarily it was to hide locations, which was a problem during the early days because of the featureless landscape; the other use was to provide some shade for the troops and vehicles which were out in the hot, dry sands.

Below: A Westland Lynx AH.7 of 654 Squadron, which is part of 4 Regiment AAC, normally based at Detmold, during a re-arming and refuelling sequence while on operations in the Gulf. In addition to the normal equipment the Lynx have been fitted with a cabin-mounted GPMG for self-protection.

Above: During the conflict two TOW equipped Lynx AH.7 would work with one Gazelle AH.1 reconnaissance helicopter in a Combat Recce Patrol. In Germany, should conflict arise it was always felt that the armoured reconnaissance would be one of a compressing line of communication in which the ground patrols would move forward or remain in position – gradually pulling back. Contacts would be reported and the Lynx would be called in to deal with the enemy vehicles.

In the Gulf, once the land battle had started the Iraqis were either surrendering or withdrawing so quickly that the roles were reversing and it was the helicopters that were doing the spotting, reporting the position back to the troops on the ground.

Right: To improve logistic support the RCT is having its transport fleet modernized. The widely used Bedford M Type will eventually be replaced by the Leyland DAF 4-tonner of which 5,350 have been ordered for delivery over a five-year period. This vehicle has a permanently engaged four-wheel drive and a spacious three-man cab together with their kit. The cab design also meets the low height requirement permitting transportation in the Hercules.

Illustrated is one of the Bedford AWD TM 6x6 trucks which have a 14-tonne capacity, seen here providing logistic capacity in the Gulf. A total of 1,045 have been supplied to the Army.

Above: Despite elaborate precautions, some damage to property during exercises is inevitable, and in BAOR Damage Controllers are an integral part of the organization. All troops are briefed before an exercise begins on ways to limit damage and the compensation that must be paid. The Damage Control teams are given reported locations of incidents and will immediately check the extent and negotiate with the injured party.

Above: The extent of damage varies according to the units involved. A squadron of Challengers on the move can cause considerable damage with their tracks to roads and crops. A platoon of infantry should cause minimal damage – here the Damage Controller takes a photograph to record damage to a stile. Sometimes the damage is not totally the Army's fault, prior damage perhaps having been inflicted or there may have been lack of maintenance. It is up to the Damage Controller to assess the true state of affairs.

Left and right: Here Chieftains have passed along a farm track and caused considerable damage on the bends. While the original track was mainly earth, the Royal Engineers making the repairs have used a quantity of hard-core which together with graders and rollers will mean that the track will be of a much higher standard than prior to the incident. This attitude will often placate the farmers who have had to endure many exercises over the years.

Right: Block paving is used in considerable quantities on the continent. When the kerbs are hit by the tracks of a MBT or APC they tend to dislodge rather than break up. Here troops from the REs recover the blocks from a damaged section of the pavement before compressing the hard-core and replacing the block paving to restore the pavement to its original condition.

Left: While Damage Controllers are concerned with physical damage, the movement of MBTs, AFVs or even wheeled vehicles will inevitably lead mud on the roads and cause a hazard. Troops are instructed to remove any deposits, but in practice they only shovel away large lumps of mud. If a number of vehicles have used a road the DamCon vehicles such as this Unimog road-sweeper will be in action.

Below left: The end of an exercise period. After several weeks of irregular sleep and primitive conditions, a return to the normal service life in barracks. For the Pipe Major of the Scots Guards it is time to bring out the bagpipes and play some stirring music.

Below: As part of maintaining good relations the end of the exercise is the time to convey thanks to the land owners.

Here the regiment's Sergeant-Major, who made the initial recce, thanks a German baron for the use of his land and outbuildings by the Army Air Corps mobile headquarters during the exercise.

Belize

Belize is a country of nearly 9,000 square miles in South America. It was originally settled during the 17th Century and became a British Colony in 1871. Known as British Honduras, it received independence in September 1981 and currently has a population approaching 180,000.

British forces initially stayed to help train the Belize Defence Force (BDF), and currently remain to deter neighbouring Guatemala from using military force to realize her claim on Belize. This is a territorial dispute which dates back for three centuries. To assist the BDF are approximately 1,600 British servicemen of whom 1,300 are Army, the rest RAF. The RAF are based at Belize City with Harriers and Pumas which are flown in support of the Army and BDF plus a Rapier battery for airfield defence.

The main role of the British Forces Belize (BFB) is deterrence and this is achieved by constant high-profile patrolling of border areas. In addition a series of static observation posts overlook potential crossing-points. These are backed up with Harrier air patrols and frequent visits by the West Indies Guard Ship (WIGS).

Should difficulties or tension arise a plan would be quickly implemented to provide reinforcements which would be flown out from the UK. Each year this is practised by the deployment of an infantry company who usually deplane and go straight into the final stages of a live firing exercise. Such is the nature of the country that exercises do not suffer from the restrictions encountered in UK and Europe. Fostering good relations with the locals is an important part of everyday life for members of the BFB. Because of limited national resources the Royal Engineer Squadron will assist in road and bridge repairs. Often the medical facilities may be called upon together with medivac by helicopters. Central America and the West Indies suffer from relatively frequent natural disasters and the BFB are usually quickly on the scene to provide relief.

Off duty Belize provides a wealth of interests including water sports on the world's second longest barrier reef which provides sailing, canoeing, windsurfing and sub-aqua diving. Inland there are an equally wide range of activities for the off-duty serviceman or woman, ranging from mountain climbing, discovering ancient Mayan ruins, searching for rare species of wild life and caving. For the even more adventurous Mexico, Costa Rica and Peru are enticing. Recently talks have progressed to the point where it looks as though the new Guatemalan president will agree to drop its claim to Belize in exchange for greater access to the Caribbean.

Left: The jungle forms a substantial part of the Belize landscape and is an ideal environment in which to develop leadership. It provides a particular challenge for junior commanders where high standards of personal skill and navigation are required in order to be able to survive and move about.

Below: Much of the countryside of west Belize consists of jungle. Patrols keep check on border areas, but because of the nature of the land and lack of roads most of the patrols are inserted and removed by helicopters. The area also has a precipitous limestone 'karst' landscape which requires careful and accurate navigation for the pilots and troops to ensure that they RV at the correct time and location.

Right: The RAF Westland-built Puma HC.1s of 1563 Flight are based with BFB HQ at Belize City Airport. Because of the nature of the country's terrain the helicopter is vital. Some of the mountain-top OPs in the south-west of Belize can only be re-supplied by helicopter. The 'replen' tasks can last all day, shuffling men and supplies from the Forward Ordnance Detachments to the OPs and jungle patrols and bringing men back.

Right: The Westland Gazelle AH.1 is the only AAC type present in Belize. Manned by members of 25 Flight and based at Airport Camp alongside Belize City Airport, the Flight provides liaison, patrol and observation. Pilots do as much flying there during their four month tour as they would normally do in twelve months in the UK.

Right: One way of moving around parts of Belize, especially to the north, is via the network of rivers. Here the Rigid Raiders come in to their own. Capable of 30 knots from their 135hp outboard motors, the Rigid Raiders normally carry about six men depending on the amount of kit.

Left: The Close Reconnaissance Troop is based at Holdfast Camp and equipped with the FV101 Scorpion CVR(T). At the time of the visit the Troop was manned by a Recce Troop of the Royal Hussars (Prince of Wales's Own). Their role is to maintain highly visible reconnaissance patrols for the benefit of the neighbouring Guatemalans.

The Scorpion can ford water obstacles of about 1 metre without any preparation. It is seen here emerging from a river. For deeper water a wading screen can be fitted and raised and the Scorpion can float and can use its tracks for propulsion.

Left: The Alvis Scorpion has proved to be a reliable, efficient and effective vehicle, more than 293 having been built for the Army. It formed the basis for a family of vehicles to meet the requirements for reconnaissance, fire support and anti-tank of which more than 2,000 have now been built for the Army. While the Scorpion is no alternative to an MBT, its speed, mobility and rate of fire make it an effective weapon in the type of terrain encountered in Belize.

Right: Men of the 1st Battalion The Royal Highland Fusiliers (Princess Margaret's Own Glasgow and Ayrshire Regiment) Milan Platoon deploy from Holdfast for training. It is claimed the Milan can penetrate more than 850mm of standard armour. This is achieved by the long spike on the missile nose which is designed to ensure that the hollow-charge warhead is detonated at the optimum distance from the target for maximum effect.

Below: Given the inaccessibility of many parts of Belize and the lack of alternative means of communication, radio is essential. Here members of 633 (Caribbean) Signals Troop check their aerials to ensure optimum reception.

Below right: The cayes off the coast of Belize and along the barrier reef provide an ideal location for R & R (Rest and Recreation) for personnel. The Joint Services Adventure Training Centre at St George's Caye provides a very pleasant setting.

Left: Members of 247 Pro Coy (Provost Company) of 2 Regiment Royal Military Police are perhaps the most visible part of the British Army presence in Berlin. Their role is to mount high-profile patrols in and around West Berlin and this has increased to include patrols into East Berlin.

Reunification has meant that these roles have all but disappeared, with patrols no longer based on the wall. The RMPs seen here are at the Soviet War Memorial near the Brandenburg Gate inside West Berlin.

Centre left: The 14,000 oppressive East German wall guards have become a token force. Gone are the armoured vehicles, and over-wall insults and taunts have been replaced by a somewhat bewildered, good-neighbourly attitude, with the Trabant car.

Below left: The Royal Welch Fusiliers is the oldest infantry regiment of Wales, having been formed by William III in 1689. Here members of 1 Battalion The Royal Welch Fusiliers' recce platoon can be seen on the Wire Patrol by Havel lake.

Below right: Based at RAF Gatow, 7 Flight AAC provides helicopter support for the Berlin Field Force with three Westland Gazelle AH.1s. Normally two of these are continuously available at two hours' notice. In an emergency this can be reduced to 30 minutes and during a period of tension would be reduced to ten minutes.

Berlin

The legacy of the Second World War was, until very recently, much more than mere memory for all of Europe. As the Allies reached Berlin in 1945 they initiated the distribution of German territory among the victors. Soviet Russia had advanced her borders extensively through the absorption of minor states, with control of Berlin the key to consolidating their victory over Germany. The Western Allies argued for its multi-national control and administration, and so it came to be occupied by British, American, French and Soviet forces, beginning more than forty years of unique military duty for the British Army. It has always been an area for British forces to experience the role of the occupying force, and also a continual demand on budget and manpower. Thus, although Berlin is now once again a united city and occupation is terminated, it is included here because it has been an important separate aspect of the British Army overseas throughout the post-war decades. With the removal of such a need, and with *Options for Change* implications, it is probable that similar commitments will feature less in the new British Army.

Right: Check-Point Charlie was once the most notable entry point into Eastern Europe. Check-Points Alpha and Bravo are at the eastern/western ends of the only corridor that the Allied troops are allowed to use for access by road to Berlin. Manned by members of the Royal Military Police as well as French and US military police, Check-Point Charlie was the main crossing-point from West Berlin into East Berlin. With the knocking down of the wall and reunification, Check-Point Charlie rapidly became a token and has now been completely removed.

Above: Spandau Forest provides one of the training areas available to the Berlin Field Force. Bordering the wall, troop training continues within earshot of the East Germans and sometimes even in sight.

To provide realistic training in urban warfare without causing disturbance to the public, an area having all the features of a section of the city was built near the Ruhleben ranges for FIBUA (Fighting In Built Up Areas) training.

Left: For construction work 38 Field Squadron is equipped with a range of German graders, bulldozers, crawler excavators and a variety of tipper trucks. Here a Hanomag 33C is digging a drainage ditch using its backhoe.

Opposite page, top: 38 Field Squadron Royal Engineers' main role is to support the Berlin Infantry Brigade. It is seen here using its Hanomag 22C and 44D in the airfield damage repair role at RAF Gatow.

Right: The British Military Train (BMT) or 'Berliner' ran from Charlottenburg in Berlin to Braunschweig in West Germany. It has been administered by the East Germans who supplied the engines and crews. The only BMT in regular service in the world, it was guarded by the Allies and assured safe passage by the Soviets.

The Americans ran two trains each day, the French three a week and the British one a day. With the reduction of tension and reunification the BMT ceased to operate on 20 November 1990.

51 80 08-80 011-3 P
WRüm

Left, centre and bottom: The GPMG is still in use in substantial numbers but is being replaced by the LSW variant of the SA80. Those accustomed to the SLR and GPMG found in the Falklands that if an enemy were hit by a 7.62mm round the kinetic energy would knock him to the ground. While the SA80 uses the lighter 5.56mm ammunition, which enables more rounds to be carried, it takes more of them to stop the enemy.

It was not until the advent of laser technology that an effective means of simulating small-arms fire could be made. The SAWES (Small Arms Weapons Effect Simulation) laser gun flashes a small beam of laser light instead of a bullet whenever the gun is fired. If this beam of light hits one of the sensors placed at various vital points of the body a sound will be emitted and that soldier is then removed from the exercise. Depending on the nature of the exercise 'casualties' would probably return after a set period to represent reinforcements.

The Royal Ordnance Simulation HQ has already designed a range of simulated weapons which include SA80, LAW, grenades, mines and tank guns.

Right: A member of the Berlin Air Defence Troop with the Javelin LML (Lightweight Multiple Launcher) training in the Spandau Forest. Besides the advantage of three missiles the LML takes a strain off the operator by maintaining the missile at the ready position without his having to hold it there. The few seconds involved in lifting the missile to shoulder position could make the difference between hitting and missing an attacking aircraft.

Right: A project to give the FV432 an offensive and fire support role produced a variant of the FV432 which was fitted with the Rarden Turret as fitted to the Fox and Scimitar. The programme did not proceed beyond the total of thirteen built and used for trials, probably because it was competing with the Scimitar for similar roles. At the end of the trials the FV432 Rarden were passed on to equip the Berlin infantry regiments.

Left: Like all other infantry battalions that have not converted to Warrior, the three Berlin infantry regiments (shortly to be reduced to two) are equipped with the FV432 armoured personnel carrier. Unlike any of the other regiments, the Berlin FV432s, together with the other combat vehicles of the Berlin Brigade, have a camouflage pattern unique within the British Army. This is due to the role in Berlin which would consist of an urban conflict and the camouflage pattern reflects this.

In the light of recent events the likelihood of the need for military intervention seems remote, and with the gradual withdrawal of units of the Berlin Field Force this form of camouflage will disappear from any vehicles in the British Army.

Left: The 14th/20th King's Hussars was formed in 1922 by the amalgamation of two light cavalry regiments, the 14th King's Hussars and the 20th Hussars. The 14th 'Dormers' Dragoons were formed in 1715 and the 20th Iniskilling Light Dragoons were raised in 1759. The two regiments gave up their horses in 1938 for tanks.

Currently the 14th/20th have eighteen urban-camouflaged Chieftain tanks based at Smutts Barracks. As a result of the reunification of Germany political tensions have dispersed and the 14th/20th will be one of the first units to leave Berlin together with an infantry battalion.

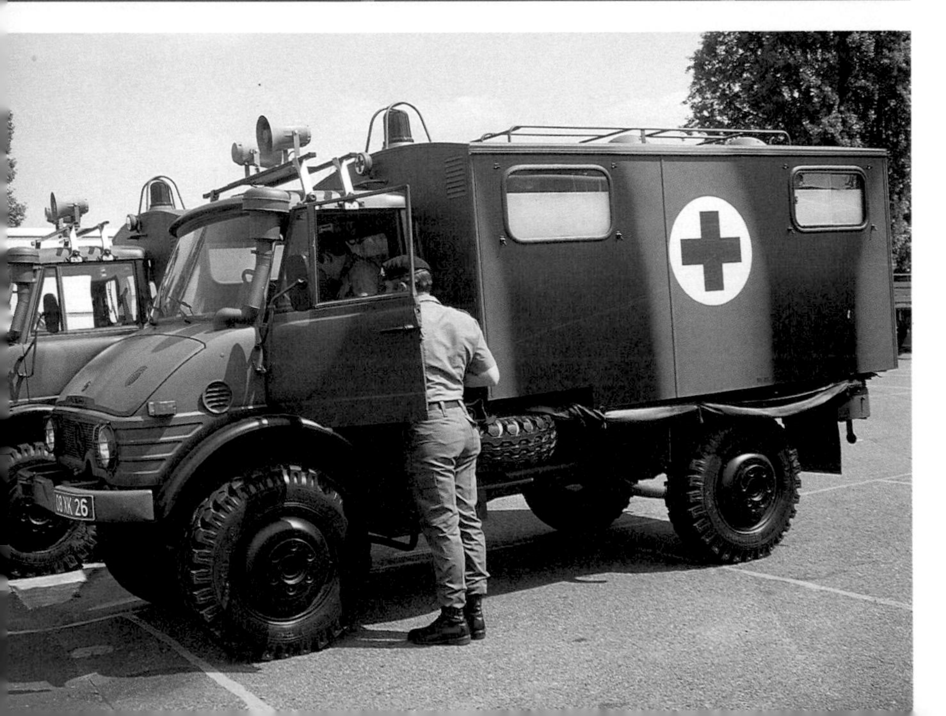

Left: Together with 38 Field Squadron RE, 62 Transport And Movements Squadron RCT, based at Alexander Barracks, are equipped with a whole range of German-built and supplied equipment provided by the German government as part of the Potsdam Agreement regarding the Allied troops stationed in Berlin. These range from Opel Kadett cars for general-purposes to a variety of MAN trucks up to 16 tonnes. The ambulance is from the Mercedes-Benz Unimag family of vehicles.

Canada

The problems of suitable training areas in Europe caused the army to look elsewhere and in 1971 they were allocated 1,000 square miles of low-grade Canadian prairie of no agricultural value near Calgary. BATUS (British Army Training Unit Suffield) is located on the Suffield Training Ground and is the location for a series of 'Medicine Man' exercises held there each year. These are in fact a series of live firing exercises for two mechanized companies, two armoured squadrons, an engineer field troop and an artillery battery. Lasting three weeks, the exercises consist of a week of special arms training followed by companies and squadrons combining to form a 'manoeuvre group', and the final week is devoted to the battle group working as a whole.

The large number of vehicles, APCs, MBTs and Artillery plus weapons remain permanently at Suffield where REME workshops keep them maintained.

Right: The essence of the training at BATUS, which is different from most other training exercises, is that live ammunition is used throughout. Safety could be a real nightmare with units progressing at different speeds and then being fired on by those behind. All weapons have a peacetime safety trace and to monitor all firings is a fleet of vehicles, manned by Range Safety Officers, including a number of brightly painted Ferret Scout Cars. In addition the Range Safety Officers have a couple of Gazelles.

Left: GPMG ammunition contains a mix of standard and tracer so that the firer can see exactly where his rounds are falling and make any necessary adjustments.

Centre left and bottom left: During the night element of the final exercise various sound effects can be heard in the distance, simulating an enemy on the move. Gradually the sounds seem to be coming closer and the firing starts.

Illum shells are fired from mortar and artillery positions behind, and as targets become visible they are fired upon by the tanks and artillery. Various explosives and thunderflashes are triggered to simulate return fire. As the enemy targets approach firing becomes more intense and the infantry join in with their anti-tank weapons. As infantry targets appear the IW and LSW sections open fire until all the targets are down.

Opposite page, top: For increased mobility the British Army has 75 Alvis Spartan APCs which are fitted with the Milan Compact Turret (MCT). Four have been issued to each mechanized and armoured infantry battalion together with their firing posts.

Opposite page, bottom: The early FV432 Mk 1 still exists in substantial numbers at BATUS, primarily to provide mechanized transport for the infantry regiments, but they are also used by most other participating units including the armoured squadrons, artillery battery, RE and range safety. Its ancestry can be traced back to the bren gun carrier of the Second World War, but in Europe it is now being replaced by the Saxon and the Warrior.

W41B
761

Left: This FV432 with the extra aerials is fitted with FACE which is used as the command post in support of the BATUS M109 to provide target details. FACE is in the process of being replaced by the hand-held GUNZEN and the BATES (Battlefield Artillery Target Engagement System) at Battery level, and this should be followed at Divisional level in 1993.

Centre left: The Royal Engineers' vehicles such as the CET are likely to carry the Maxi packs of fascines. Smaller Mini packs can be carried by many types of vehicle, such as the FV432 seen here, and even by helicopters, to provide an instant method of crossing ditches. By using several packs gaps of up to 3m deep and 15 metres wide can be crossed by wheeled and tracked vehicles.

Bottom left: Some FV432s are fitted

with the GPMG turret for self-defence. This turret is mounted on the circular main roof hatch which is permanently closed. The turret contains the 7.62mm GPMG and it has additional smoke-dischargers. When shut down aiming is through a periscopic sight. In addition to a full 360° traverse the GPMG can be elevated to about 50° for anti-aircraft defence.

Right: One of the important roles of the Gazelle is that of observation. As can be seen here the pilot positions the helicopter so that the observer can get a good view of the objective without being seen. With his radio the observer can keep the commanders informed as to the current situation and potential developments, before moving off discreetly to another position. It may be that the situation requires radio silence or radio jamming is taking place in which case the Gazelle can rapidly fly to the commander's location. If the Gazelles are part of the anti-tank squadrons the observers would be briefing the Lynx pilots before they move into position to destroy the armour.

Below: Having deployed from their FV432, troops advance on their objective. Ten fully equipped men can be carried by the FV432 but with a maximum speed of 52km/hr (on roads) it is now considered sluggish when compared to the Warrior. It is also very weak in the fire support role compared to its modern counterpart, especially during the initial vital minutes of deploying when it would be useful to be able to keep the enemies' heads down.

42
42

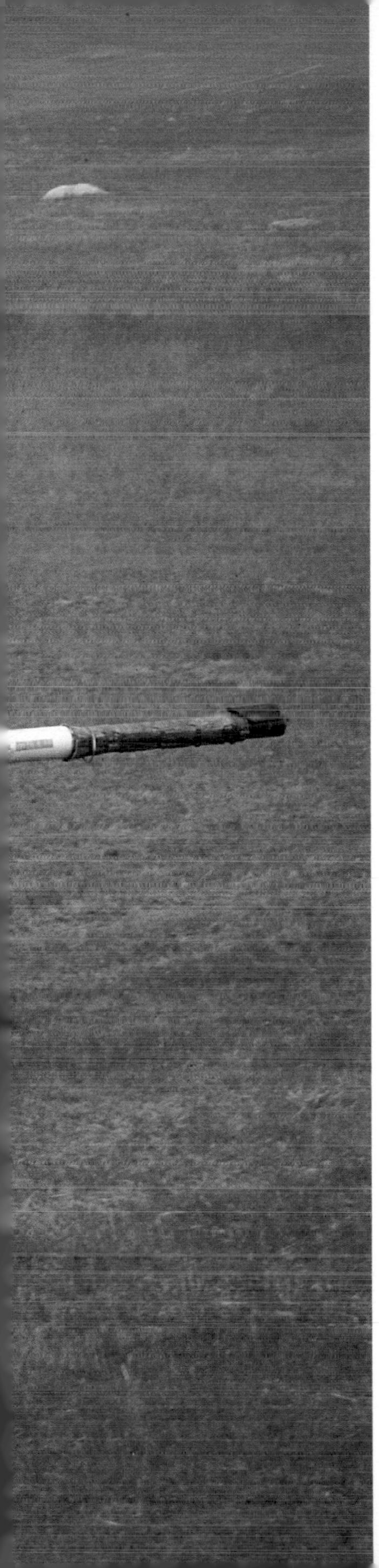

Left: One of the main early criticisms of Chieftain was that it had insufficient power. The L60 engine was selected early in the design stage to meet the Army's requirement for a multi-fuel engine. With hindsight this was not a good decision, the early engines being underpowered, giving 650bhp instead of 700bhp. By the time this had been corrected the Chieftain had increased in weight so that even more power was needed. Having said that, the fire-control currently fitted has proved to be such that the crew have a good chance of a first-round kill. Thus the Chieftain, while less manoeuvrable than some of its contemporaries, has better armour and better firepower.

Top right: A column of Chieftains approaches a replen site during Exercise 'Medicine Man'. The Chieftain has been a heavily armoured tank following the tradition of the Centurion. The Improved Fire Control System has upgraded the aiming and ranging of the gun to give a reasonable chance of a first-round kill up to 10,000 metres. Armour, especially around the turret, has also been improved to enable it to withstand a certain amount of punishment.

Above: The Chieftain can carry 64 rounds of ammunition for its 120mm main gun plus 6,000 rounds of 7.62mm for its two machine-guns. The main ammunition is supplied in three parts: detonator (about the size of a shot-gun cartridge); bags of explosive; shell. The separately loaded ammunition gives more room for the loader to manoeuvre thus permitting a smaller turret. The weights being split means that he will not tire so quickly from repeated loading.

Left: The M109 is manned by a crew of six plus two men who follow in the ammunition limber. The driver normally drives with the front hatch open, but in action the hatch is closed and the driver assumes the reclining position using periscopes and NBC protection. In dry conditions the disadvantage of being exposed is the airborne dust especially when driving in convoy.

Below: The US-built M109 has been quite successful, about 2,000 serving with some thirty armies worldwide. It has quite a large turret which gives a reasonable amount of room for the gun crew. The hull and turret are built from aluminium which gives better amphibious capability than other similar types of vehicle.

Right: The FV432 can be a useful mortar platform when a special table mounting is fitted which gives a full 360° traverse. Once fitted only the barrel and sight need to be assembled. The normal baseplate and the support are stowed should the mortar require dismounting. The FV432 has space for up to 160 bombs and requires a crew of six for this role.

Below: The FV107 Scimitar is powered by the Jaguar J60 engine which develops 190bhp and enables it to reach speeds of up to 80.5km/h on the road. It is seen here refuelling from a Bedford 4-tonne truck equipped with the UBRE (Unit Bulk Replenishment Equipment). The Scimitar has a capacity of 423 litres of fuel which can give it a range of up to 644 kilometres.

Left: Should casualties be substantial a number of vehicles are readily converted to the ambulance role, one of which being the FV432 which is likely to augment the specialized wheeled 1-tonne Land Rover ambulance and tracked Spartan.

Left: The FV4204 Chieftain ARV first emerged in prototype form in 1971, the first production ARV appearing in 1974. The ARV is basically a Mk 5 hull with the front redesigned to accommodate two winches with a pull of 30,000 and 3,000 kilograms. For self-defence the ARV has a cupola-mounted 7.62 machine gun and twelve smoke-dischargers.

With the introduction of the Challenger, the REME FV434 was found to be unable to cope with the 5.49-tonne engine pack. As a result the Chieftain ARRV evolved as a conversion of the Chieftain ARV with the addition of the Atlas hydraulic crane and an engine stand at the rear. The ARRV has only a limited repair capability and is really an interim measure until sufficient deliveries of the Challenger ARRV enter service.

Left: The FV434 is the maintenance variant of the FV432 family of vehicles. Here it is recovering a disabled FV432 on the BATUS training ground at Suffield. It is crewed by a commander, driver (who doubles as the crane operator) and two mechanics. For defensive purposes the FV434 is fitted with a 7.62mm Bren LMG or the 7.62 GPMG.

Above: An MBT that has broken down instantly becomes a liability, being vulnerable to attack. It is, therefore, of vital importance that all vehicles be cleaned, checked and maintained so that they are always fully serviceable. These Chieftains are being serviced by their crews at the end of a 'Medicine Man' exercise at BATUS.

Right: The US-designed and built M578 has a similar hull to the M107 but has a turret and crane fitted at the rear. Designed to support the M107, M109 and M110 Self-Propelled Howitzers, it is in service with the US, British and other NATO armies including the British Army. The M578 has a crew of three: the driver sits at the front with the engine on his right; the other two members sit in the turret and have the Browning Machine-Gun for self-defence. The M578 has been designed to lift the heavy engine packs of the SP Howitzers and can recover vehicles weighing up to approximately 30,000 kilograms.

Left: At the end of yet another 'Medicine Man' exercise the band strikes up and Camp Crowfoot is full of music – a contrast to the noise of armoured vehicles and explosions that have been the norm for the last few weeks.

Left: On the prairie, a Major of the Royal Scots Dragoon Guards exchanges his Chieftain for the unit bike. When the regiment gets back to Germany they will return to their Challengers. The value of these exercises is enormous – less than six months after this exercise the regiments had been deployed to the Gulf as part of Operation 'Granby'.

Cyprus

Two Sovereign Base Areas (SBAs) in Cyprus provide home for 2,300 servicemen who man an armoured reconnaissance squadron, two infantry battalions, an AAC flight and all engineering support. The Eastern SBA contains Dhekelia and Ayios Nikolaios and the Western SBA Episkopi and Akrotiri. While these are kept separate from the UN peace-keeping forces (UNFICYP), they can be made available as a reserve should events require additional support.

The SBAs were retained when Cyprus was given independence in 1960 and the troops have remained there ever since. With the introduction of the UN peace-keeping force, the Army units have provided general support and support for the UN Interim Forces in Lebanon (UNIFIL). During Operation 'Granby' the airfield at RAF Akrotiri provided a vital link for aircraft en route or returning from the Gulf. Areas of reserve storage were created and as a result the regiments involved in security at the Sovereign Bases Areas (SBA) were working in top gear.

Right: A patrol from 3 Queens check a valley in the western SBA (Sovereign Base Area).

Far right: Throughout his term of service an infantryman receives training and his skill is constantly tested. Here a soldier is having to approach an objective while avoiding enemy patrols.

Left: On completion of the course the soldier is marked on his skill at arms. In this test weapon holding, reactions and firing position are deemed to be the most important. However, consideration must be given to field craft, observation and cover. Failure to reach a certain standard will require the soldier to undertake further training.

Below: Each of the infantry regiments has Milan and 3 Queens is no exception. Here the Milan Platoon have positioned themselves in a commanding view of a valley near Episkopi.

Right: The Mortar Platoon of 3 Queens during a training exercise in scrub land near Episkopi. For training purposes two types of mortar bomb can be used. The first is a sand-filled bomb with a small charge which has a range of only 80 metres and is reusable. The other – which is being used here – is a completely inert bomb which is inserted in the normal way but drops out the bottom of the cut-away Slipper Barrel.

Below: 'B' Squadron, 17th/21st Lancers have been providing the recce patrol around the western SBA. Based at Episkopi, they are equipped with the Ferret Scout Car and the FV601(C) Saracen Armoured Car.

The FV601 Saladin Armoured Car design originated in 1947 around the chassis for the proposed Humber 1-ton 4x4 family of vehicles. Built by Alvis after a protracted development, the FV601(C) entered production in 1958 and continued until 1972. It is fitted with a 76mm gun plus a 7.62mm co-axial Browning machine-gun in the turret and an additional Browning on top of the turret by the commander's hatch. Originally issued to Regular and Territorial Reserve armoured car regiments, the Saladin has been largely replaced by the Scorpion. The Saladin has been used operationally in Aden, Borneo, Japan, North Africa and Malaya and has been widely exported, especially to the Middle East. Apart from a few examples used for training, the Saladins in Cyprus are the last remaining in service.

Below right: The recce unit based in Cyprus must be the last major front-line unit still to be equipped with the Ferret Scout Car. Even older than the Saladin, the Ferret surfaced in prototype form in 1950 and by 1971 when production finished a total of 4,409 had been built.

MILITARY POLICE
STOP
CHECK
POINT

Opposite page, top: The Army issues medals in recognition of a variety of achievements by its officers and men. The presentation of medals is usually made by a senior officer, in this case the Commander British Forces Cyprus, who is presenting members of 'B' Squadron, 17th/21st Lancers with medals for Long Service, for serving in Northern Ireland and with the United Nations peacekeeping force.

Opposite page, bottom: During peacetime the Royal Military Police operate in a similar role to the civilian police, including general police duties and the Special Investigation Branch. In wartime their role is traffic control to ensure that road signs are correct and lost vehicles or units are re-routed.

Top right: During the First World War pack horses were commonly used, and even as recently as the Second World War their numbers were substantial. Their services were finally dispensed with in the early 1970s. However, the pack horse has been re-discovered and has returned to service in Cyprus where the nature of the countryside has shown that there is still room for him in the modern army.

Centre right: Sport is always a popular feature of service life and opportunities exist for most forms wherever the army is based. Polo is popular among cavalry and reconnaissance regiments such as the 17th/21st Lancers, here seen playing the 13th/18th Royal Hussars who like to keep their traditional horse-riding skills.

Bottom right: In Cyprus the weather and scenery provide some excellent off-duty activities. A popular duo is to ski on the snow at the top of the Troodos in the morning followed by water skiing in the seas off Episkopi in the afternoon. A more conventional and popular sport is sailing along the beautiful Cypriot coastline.

Above: The UNFICYP Headquarters and BRITCON HQ are both located at the old Nicosia RAF camp. One of UNFICYP's problems is that it has only a six months' mandate. Towards the end of each period a new decision is made as to whether withdraw or retain the Force. As a result very little planning can be made to provide anything much more than day-to-day consumables. Many of the buildings are rather basic and furniture and office equipment is becoming dilapidated; there being little incentive to invest in a location which could be vacated within six months.

Left: The UN Force Scout Car Squadron, manned by 110 men of 'C' Squadron, 9th/12th Royal Lancers, is tasked to provide UNFICYP with armoured cars to support each sector's patrol programmes, and also forms the force reserve.

The Buffer Zone (BZ) runs from the north-west of the island near Kato Pyrgos through to Dherinia at the eastern end. It runs through the middle of Nicosia where the two Scout Cars are seen driving along what is known as the Green Line. The buildings in this zone have remained untouched since the invasion.

United Nations

The Army provides the British Government's contribution to the United Nations Peace-keeping Force, the most recent contribution following the withdrawal of forces from the Gulf when a monitoring team was deployed along the Iraq/Kuwait border. The Army provided twenty officers to UNIKOM (United Nations Iraq-Kuwait Observation Mission) which had a strength of 300 when it deployed. Their role was to monitor the demilitarized zone and deter violations of its boundary. Another detachment is at the UN MFO in the Sinai Desert.

Currently, the main commitment for the Army is in Cyprus where some 700 officers and men are deployed. While Cyprus makes an ideal holiday island, there has been a history of civil unrest between the Turkish and Greek Cypriots since 1963. The following year UNFICYP (United Nations Force In Cyprus) was established with a strength of 6,200. Slowly, with the reduction of tension, elements were posted to the UN Emergency Force (UNEF II) located in the Middle East.

On 15 July 1974 the Greeks staged a *coup* against the Cypriot Government, followed five days later by an invasion force from Turkey. Since that time the island has been split into the Greek-Cypriot and the Turkish Cypriot sectors. The Turkish-Cypriots account for approximately one-fifth of the island's population and occupy about one-third of the land. Turkey maintains approximately 30,000 troops in this sector which declared itself a separate state in 1983 although this was only recognized by Ankara.

UNFICYP comprises contingents from Denmark (DANCON), Canada (CANCON) and Austria (AUSCON) as well as from Britain (BRITCON). In addition, Australia and Sweden have sent civilian police. In total 2,159 soldiers are currently deployed of whom some 700 are British. The BRITCON comprises half an infantry battalion, a field car squadron and an AAC flight.

Recently extra effort has been made by the UK and US to resolve the Greek/Turkish problem because it, and the in-fighting of member countries, is affecting NATO and especially the new Rapid Reaction Force. In 1988 the Nobel Peace Prize was awarded to the UN Peace-keeping Forces.

Right: British Ferret Scout Cars provide the Force reserve and can often be seen on patrol in sectors other than that policed by BRITCON. Here a visit is made to the members of CANCON (CANadian CONtingent).

Above: The British Sector of the BZ has twelve permanently manned OPs, fifteen temporarily manned and a further fifteen unmanned along its 34-kilometre stretch from the Canadian Sector just east of Nicosia westwards to the Danes. Each OP has a UN flag which is floodlit at night.

The duties of the soldiers manning the OPs include keeping a watchful eye on both sides to ensure that any potential trouble-spot is identified and resolved before the situation gets out of hand. In front of this OP on the outskirts of Nicosia is a fortified house which is a Turkish position.

Left: To support UNFICYP communications is vital and so 644 Signal Troop was reformed on 20 July 1964, having previously served in Aden. After the conflict the Troop was enlarged and retitled 254 (UNFICYP) Signal Squadron which had also previously served in Aden.

The Squadron is responsible for the radio, telegraph and telephone from HQ UNFICYP to the Sector Headquarters and within the UNPA. It also provides tactical communications for the Force Commander and his staff. The Squadron is commanded by a British major and a second in command, with an Austrian staff officer and a Canadian troop commander. British and Canadian signallers of all ranks make the numbers up to a total strength of 70.

Right: All UN patrols in the BZ are of an overt nature. This is a policing job and it is important that it be seen to be effective by both sides. To the west of Nicosia are some fertile areas and while much of this has been left untouched apart from the patrols, during recent years farmers have been allowed to sow sections of the BZ with crops and plant orange groves. Even this can cause difficulties at times. Recently the Greek-Cypriot farmers placed large numbers of beehives in the orange grove plantations only to have complaints from the Turks that the bees were causing them a problem.

Right: To give air support to UNFICYP the Army Air Corps (AAC) maintains a Flight of three Westland Gazelle AH.1s together with support at the UNPA at Nicosia. The role of these helicopters is to cover the daily tasks of observation, reconnaissance, control, liaison and casualty evacuation for which two are normally always available.

Right: '8' Squadron, RCT is part of the 306-strong Support Regiment of BRITCON. Besides the RCT this regiment comprises members of RAMC, REME, Royal Signals, RAOC and the AAC. In addition to normal duties the role of the RCT is to keep the numerous OPs supplied and to ensure that Greek families living in the Turkish Sector receive everything they need, and the same for the Turks in the Greek Sector.

Above: UN patrols are not without danger. This Ferret Scout Car was on patrol in the British Sector when it drove over an anti-tank mine. Initially tension rose when it was thought that it had been recently laid, but investigations proved that the mine had been laid during the 1974 invasion and that the route taken by the Scout Car was very seldom used and previous users had been lucky. Fortunately injuries were slight although the Scout Car was a write-off.

Left: Efficient provisioning is vital to any army unit, but possibly none more so than with BRITCON. Here a small unit with limited resources is spread over a large area at a number of individual, isolated locations.

Below: Among the equipment operated by the UN Fire Section at Nicosia is an ancient fire tender, affectionately known as 'Trumpton', which is based on the old Bedford RL. Probably built during the 1950s, it entered service with UNFICYP in 1969. This is not typical of the vintage of the UNFICYP equipment, but it is something of an indicator of their problems.

The Falklands

The British Army has maintained a low-key Royal Marines presence on the Falklands for many years. It was not until the invasion by the Argentinians on 2 April 1982 that most people even knew where the Falklands were. But with the invasion came a demonstration of the ability of the UK to protect its out of area commitments. Despite the vast distances involved and the absence of any local Allied location to step off from, Operation 'Corporate' proceeded remarkably well.

Once the war was over the British Government embarked on the 'Fortress Falklands' campaign with a large manning level, visibly to warn any potential aggressor that a 'repeat' would not be so easy. By the late 1980s the installation of radar and the new airfield at RAF Mount Pleasant were complete and manpower was reduced to about 1,000 which is made up of a garrison of infantry, engineers and RAF units.

Currently the Forces in the Falklands are occupied with improving the lines of communications in an area of land where roads are non-existent and even tracks are few and far between. A road has been built between Stanley and RAF Mount Pleasant and on the port complex, with another branching off to Estancia House. One of the current projects has been to build a road up to the top of Mount Kent to service the radar complex which until now has had to rely on helicopters and tracked vehicles.

Right: Bristows operate a Sikorsky S.61N helicopter as a shuttle bus around the Falkland Islands in view of the virtual non-existence of any form of road except between Stanley and Mount Pleasant. At various times the Army has had Scout, Gazelle and Lynx based at Stanley, but these have been withdrawn and the RAF provides the bulk of helicopter support with Sea Kings and Chinooks. Although primarily for civilian use, the S.61N does provide some extra capacity for the army when required.

Left: Because of the large expanses of uninhabited open country it is necessary for the Resident Infantry Company (RIC) to provide patrols throughout the Falkland Islands. The purpose of these patrols is to reassure the island residents, who have a very isolated existence, that they are secure. They also check for aggressors or infiltrators.

Left: The Falkland Islands have large numbers of defences remaining from the War. Here the RIC patrol rest briefly in an old Argentinian gun position. There are large numbers of artefacts on the battlefields which are being left for future visitors to see.

Left: In addition to the patrols around the islands, the RIC, who at the time of this visit were the Waterloo Company, 1st Battalion Duke of Wellington's Regiment (1 DWR), are required to maintain patrols around the various military installations. Here the patrol is checking the fuel tanks in a compound near RAF Mount Pleasant.

Above and right: For the infantry soldier range practice is an important aspect of his training. Even on the isolated outpost of the Falklands, target practice on the range is still a regular occurrence. Although the range is somewhat basic, the targets have that Regular Army appearance.

Left: Following the issue of a contract in 1974, the Hagglund & Soner BV.206 was developed for the Swedish Defence Material Administration to replace the Volvo BV.202. The BV.206 is designed for over-snow operation but is also fully amphibious, the tracks providing propulsive power in the water.

The BV.206 normally consists of two tracked units linked together by a steering unit. The front unit is fitted with the engine and transmission. In addition to the driver it can carry five men or 600 kilograms of cargo. The second unit can carry eleven men or 1,400 kilograms of cargo. The BV.206 is an ideal vehicle for Arctic conditions and is always to be seen in Northern Flank exercises. It is also useful in areas of soft terrain such as the extensive soft peat in the Falklands and was also used in the Gulf. The BV.206 seen here is used on the Falklands by the JSEOD team and carries their Wheelbarrow in the second unit.

Left: The main role of the Joint Service Explosives Ordnance Disposal (JSEOD) unit, which is manned by Royal Engineers from 33 Engineer Regiment (EOD), is to deal with the 117 Argentinian minefields around Darwin, Fitzroy, Fox Bay, Goose Green, Port Howard and Stanley. They also have to deal with any located munitions which include missiles, bombs, shells, grenades, flares and ammunition. The quantities and nature of the various types of ordnance deposited during the conflict will pose a problem for many years. One of the worst problems is the plastic mine; despite a great deal of effort no foolproof method of detecting it has yet been developed.

Right: Another technique for destroying the mines is to place a piece of plastic explosive on the mine and fire it remotely. While this is relatively simple, the fact that one mine is visible can mean that there are others that are not.

Right: Once the plastic explosive has been put in place and the detonator wired up, the charge is detonated with quite some effect. Mine clearance is labour intensive, and detection techniques are as yet imperfect so it is not surprising that the risk factor is considered too great. Meanwhile the mines on the beaches continue to drift and mines in the peat bogs will also inevitably shift.

Right: In some areas, such as the town of Stanley, it would be unthinkable not to check as thoroughly as practicable for mines or other explosives. Here members of the JSEOD are making final checks using Doctor Forster Forex mine-detector before this land is made available for the children of Stanley as a play area. Since the liberating of the Falkland Islands the JSEOD team has dealt with well in excess of 2.5 million items of munitions ranging from mines to bombs – the majority having been small-arms ammunition.

Above left: The skill of the Royal Engineers is especially appreciated in the Falklands where workshop facilities are in short supply. The main role of the Falkland Island Field Squadron, manned by 34 Field Squadron, is Airfield Damage Repair. But it is also tasked with repair of the essential services of water, electricity and fuel, construction engineering support for buildings, roads, under-water pipelines, and radar installations. These are in addition to the normal Field Squadron tasks of combat engineering and infantry assignments of minefield-laying and clearance, water supply, demolition, guarding vital installations and patrolling.

Above: A further workshop facility is that of blacksmithing which can turn out basic metal forming for its customers.

Left: The Falkland Islands Field Squadron manned by 34 Field Squadron, RE have a sign-making facility which is in great demand.

Right and centre right: A major task for the RE in the Falklands is the establishing of lines of communication between the various installations. Away from the hills, virtually the whole of the island is covered in peat which makes most forms of wheeled transport almost impossible. A number of stone quarries have been established at various points on the island and the crushed rock is collected and driven to the location in 10-tonne Haulamatics. In the hills are seams of rock which is being excavated and crushed. The REs use 10-tonne Haulamatics to fetch and dump the rock along surveyed routes, bulldozing it into the peat to form roads. The rough, crushed rock take its toll of tyres which require constant maintenance, as do the vehicles which are being shaken to pieces by the extreme and incessant pounding.

Right: The only hospital on the Falklands is King Edward Memorial Hospital in Stanley, but the MPC has a Medical Centre. At the end of the conflict the existing hospital was extended by the Gurkhas but it caught fire and was destroyed in 1987 so a new building was constructed. This is a joint military/civilian hospital. Most of the patients are from the fishing fleets that operate around the islands and arrive by ship or helicopter. The Queen Alexander's Royal Nursing Corps (QARNC) Nursing Officer is an Army captain and is seen here attending to the captain of a Russian fishing vessel.

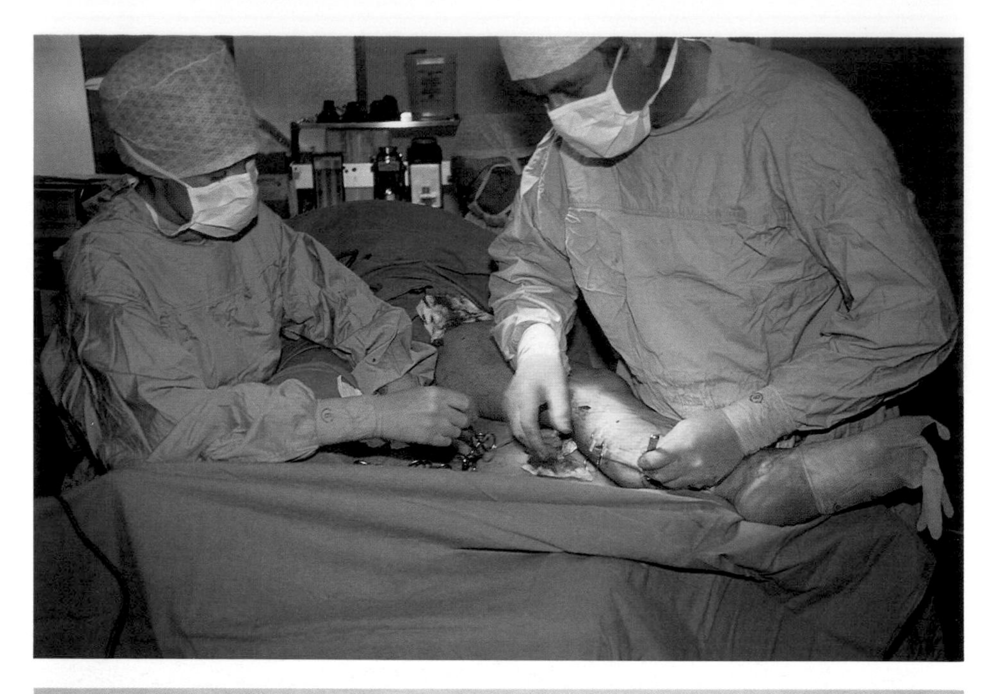

Left: The staff of the operating theatre are all members of the Royal Army Medical Corps; the patient is a civilian who has been suffering from varicose veins.

Below: 460 Port Troop, RCT is based at East Cove and operates a variety of craft to distribute stores arriving by ship from the UK. The LCVP (Landing Craft Vehicles and Personnel) are normally carried by the Assault Ships HMSS *Intrepid* and *Fearless*. They can carry 35 troops or two Land Rovers. The Mare Harbour facility was designated as the reception point for the supplies needed to build the airfield and the large complex at Mount Pleasant.

Bottom left: The multi-purpose Mexeflote pontoon can be used as a lighterage raft in harbours and at sea. Linked together the pontoons can be used as causeways, jetties or floating platforms.

The Mexeflote system features three basic components: for a lighterage raft the front or bow section consists of wedge-shaped ramps which can be raised or lowered by nearly a metre according to requirements; the centre component is made up of a series of box sections and the rear or stern pontoon contains the power unit. The causeway, jetty or floating platform would be made up of the required number of centre pontoons linked together either end to end or side to side. A Mexeflote, five sections wide and six long (one ramp, four centre and one motor) can carry more than 200 tonnes – equivalent to three Class 60 tanks. Its only limiting factor is the sea state.

Right: The soldiers of the Port Regiments engage in all aspects of dock work wherever they are based. A soldier of 460 Port Troop at East Cove is below deck moving pallets of cement ready to be craned out. During the build-up to the Gulf War 52 Port Troop, based at Al Jubail, were working in ships' holds in a measured temperature of 140F and were having to drink 5 litres of water an hour. Back in the UK, 17 Port Squadron based at Marchwood handled in excess of 70 ships during all phases of the Gulf War and probably achieved a workload that would normally be expected over two and a half years.

Right: In use at the port facility in the Falklands are two Volvo BM4400 Tractors. Based on the commercial range, the BM4400 can have alternative attachments. These vehicles have the parallel forks for pallet moving, but can be fitted with an earth-moving bucket. The cab is easily removable to facilitate airlifting under a Chinook.

Left: Security patrols manned by the Queen's Gurkha Engineers include the checking of small craft in the Sino/Hong Kong border waters in Starling Inlet off Sha Tau Kok. Here spot-checks are made of identity papers of crews bringing goods from Communist China.

Left: Looking out from the OP at Kong Shan can be seen the village of Changjie in the foreground from which a track leads left to the border fence. This crossing-point is known as International Bridge. Behind Changjie is the town, and Laingtang and Aoxia West.

Left: The Sino/Hong Kong border has some quite high hills and OPs are usually positioned on these. Here the OP at Kong Shan overlooks a Chinese PAP barracks.

Hong Kong

Hong Kong has been the British Army's largest presence outside the NATO area. With a strength of 4,900, make-up here is strongly reliant on the Gurkhas who provide three of the four infantry battalions together with the Gurkha signals, engineer and transport regiments. The forces in Hong Kong are supported by an AAC squadron.

A further Gurkha battalion together with an AAC flight is maintained in Brunei and is funded by the Sultan of Brunei. A battalion has been maintained there since 1962 when, while still a British Protectorate, a revolt broke out which was suppressed by Gurkhas who were based in Singapore at the time.

The Gurkhas have been part of the British Army since the Treaty of Segauli in 1916 and the declaration of perpetual friendship between Britain and Nepal. At the same time Britain acquired the right to recruit Nepalese citizens into her Army. The Brigade of Gurkhas comprises five battalions of infantry of which one is based in the UK. In addition there are a squadron, a support squadron and a boat troop of Engineers of which one squadron is in the UK. There are three squadrons of Signals and three of Transport, a Headquarters and a Training Depot. With the exception of those mentioned as being based elsewhere, the Brigade of Gurkhas, whose strength is in excess of 8,000, is based in Hong Kong apart from British Gurkhas Nepal whose primary role is recruiting. In 1997 Hong Kong will be transferred to China.

Right: 660 Squadron are the last operators of the Westland Scout AH.1 outside the UK. Here an officer is dropped off at Kong Shan OP. The buildings in the background are in Communist China.

Left, below and bottom: The soldiers manning these OPs are maintaining British sovereignty, and waiting to apprehend illegal immigrants trying to cross over from China. For this role they are supplied with high-powered binoculars. These men of the 7th Duke of Edinburgh's Own Gurkha Rifles (7GR) are overlooking the Chinese city of Aoxia.

Top: The Sino/Hong Kong border has a double fence topped with barbed wire between which is a floodlit road. OPs or watch towers are positioned at frequent intervals.

Above: The Border watch and patrols are assisted by an electronic system called Vindicator. This consists of wires running the entire length of the fence on which small microphones are fitted. These pick up sound from anything touching the fence and indicate the location on a control panel at the OP. The duty officer alerts the nearest patrol who investigate. The system has helped to catch a number of IIs (Illegal Immigrants), but high winds and rain cause numerous false alarms.

Right: An II climbs up the border fence and through the coiled barbed wire at the top. At the bottom of the picture to the right of the letter 'A' can be seen one of the Vindicator microphones.

Left: While the patrols have Land Rovers at their disposal, mountain bikes have also been issued. Because the majority of the area is so quiet the approaching Land Rover can be heard for quite some distance and by the time it arrives at the location the II can be hidden some distance away.

Below left: The Border guards have dogs which are used to track IIs who have managed to climb over the fence.

Below: An II is apprehended and will be taken back to HQ for interrogation after which he will be taken to a detention centre and eventually returned to the Chinese authorities. Hong Kong would be unable to cope with the numbers of Chinese who try to enter the Colony, and their presence would have a destabilizing effect. During 1987-9 22,000 illegal immigrants were arrested.

Right: As part of an agreement with China, in the endeavour to stem the flood of illegal immigrants into Hong Kong, those caught are returned. Here police vehicles stop at the border where the IIs are handed back at Man Kam To.

Below: While the Sino/Hong Kong border crosses a number of hills to the east, most of the border follows the river. In some places the level of pollution has been so great that those IIs who have tried to swim across have either died in the river or collapsed on reaching the Hong Kong shore.

Left: New recruits at the Training Depot for the Brigade of Gurkhas at Sek Kong. In preparation for 1997, when all the Gurkhas will have been withdrawn from Hong Kong, the Gurkha regiments are adopting the pace and drill movements of the Light Division. This will introduce a degree of uniformity which will be required when serving alongside other troops of the Light Division when in the UK.

Below: Gurkha junior NCOs receive refresher field instruction following a course on tactics, before applying them on a training area in the hills behind Sek Kong. In the background can be seen the Chinese family burial urns which are located along one edge of the training area.

Right: During the training exercise a Gurkha runs with his LSW (Light Support Weapon) at the ready during the junior NCOs Cadre section attacks. The LSW is the replacement for the GPMG. Belonging to the SA80 family of weapons, the LSW fires the 5.62mm ammunition as does the IW with which 80 per cent of the parts are interchangeable. It is considerably lighter than the GPMG, 6.88 kilograms as against 11.77 kilograms. It has a longer, heavier barrel which gives it an effective range of 600 metres and can fire 675-725 rounds per minute.

Below: The SA80 IW is fitted with the SUSAT (Sight Unit, Small Arms, Trilux) sight system which is, in effect, a high-performance 4x magnification inline telescope enabling accurate firing at ranges of up to 500 metres. The Kite sight can be substituted to give a night vision capability.

5
3
3
32BA39
25
05FF95
26
05FF05

Opposite page, top: The Gurkhas of 28 Gurkha Transport Regiment (GTR) are probably the last regular users of the FV603 Saracen which originally was designed as an APC for troop transport with overhead protection, following the highlighting of a need during the Malaysian emergency. Based on the Saladin chassis production towards the end of 1952, the Saracen can carry ten troops in addition to its two crewmen. For self-defence it has a turret with a .30 machine-gun although the gun is not now normally carried. The Saracen has had success with variants including the ambulance role and artillery command vehicle, and has had wide export sales. As the FV432 entered service the Saracen started to decline from front-line regiments and passed to the TA, driving schools and research establishments.

The GTR provides all second-line military transport support in the Territory, and is responsible for driver training and upgrading throughout the Brigade of Gurkhas. The regiment comprises two Gurkha battalions and one squadron from the Hong Kong Military Service Corps.

Opposite page, bottom: Increasing troubles in Northern Ireland saw the return to front-line use of the Saracen as the main APC for units based there. They were up-armoured and modified with a variety of anti-riot equipment. The majority of the Saracens now remaining serve with 28 GTR in the civil disturbance role.

Right, top and centre: Dogs from the Hong Kong Defence Animal Support Unit are used in riot control. To help contain a potentially ugly situation the handlers have a radio in their helmet and can be briefed on the situation by their controller who has the benefit of being outside the affray.

Above: A Gurkha dog-handler with his Arms and Explosive Search Dog. These dogs are specially trained to sniff out explosives. They are usually used to hunt for terrorist bombs or illegal arms shipments.

Above left and right: The Royal Gurkha Signals is based in Hong Kong to provide the communications for the Headquarters British Forces and the Garrison unit, and the military radio network for command and control of the Territory in an emergency. Part of the communications network is the permanent military telephone network, part of which can be seen being checked.

HMS *Tamar* is the location for the Headquarters British Forces Hong Kong, and the Gurkha Signals provide the communications between the UK, Hong Kong, Brunei and Nepal. A member of the Gurkha Signal Regiment can be seen operating the long haul radio telex.

Left: Men of the 1st Battalion Duke of Edinburgh's Royal Regiment (1 DERR) man their 81mm Mortar during a training exercise in the old fort site behind their barracks at Stanley. 1 DERR was formed on 9 June 1959 from the amalgamation of the former Royal Berkshire Regiment (Princess Charlotte of Wales's) and the Wiltshire Regiment (Duke of Edinburgh's). Under the Options for Change the regiment will merge once again – this time with the 'Glorious' Gloucestershire Regiment. Since these photographs were taken the regiment has returned to the UK and is now part of 24 AMB; they have been replaced by the 1st Battalion, The Royal Regiment of Wales.

The 81mm Mortar provides integral indirect fire support at battalion level, having a range of between 100 and 5,800 metres. It can be broken down into three pieces weighing less than 13 kilograms. A variant of the FV432 has been fitted for firing the 81mm Mortar through the circular roof hatch, and has storage racking for 160 bombs.

Above and right: A section of The Duke of Edinburgh's Royal Regiment patrol the hills behind Stanley and parts of the shanty town along the nearby coast.

Opposite page, top: Two snipers in their full camouflage Ghillie suits being briefed about their targets on the sniper range at Hong Kong by a QMSI instructor from the SASC (Small Arms School Corps) while an officer from 6GR looks on.

The two men are from the Australian Army 8/9 RAR on exchange. Exchanges of personnel from different countries broadens the outlook and good ideas are shared; it also helps to improve the understanding of why similar units operate in different ways. Its benefits were demonstrated during the Gulf War.

Opposite page, bottom: A sniper has to get himself into position without having been seen, and may have to stay there fully alert for a long time, waiting for the opportunity to fire.

Camouflage is very important as is the choice of weapon. The M85 Sniper Rifle has been designed to have a 100 per cent first shot capability at ranges of up to 600 metres. Anything less than this might mean that he would have to take several shots, alerting his target and perhaps blowing his cover. The new sniper rifle is the L96 which is a 7.62mm calibre weapon.

Above right and right. Because of the confined nature of Hong Kong, a range has been designed and built on Stonecutters Island where it is virtually impossible for a stray round to ricochet off the range.

Right: The Hong Kong Military Service Corps, though having had several titles, has an unbroken history dating back to 1943, although its soldiers have served with the British Army since 1890. When Hong Kong fell in 1941 the locally enlisted men were ordered to disperse to their homes, but many made their way into China where they joined the British Army Aid Group. In 1943 some volunteered for further service and were enlisted into the Border and Gloucestershire Regiments. Later they saw active service in Burma. In 1984 the Corps moved from Lyemun Barracks to Stonecutters Island. Here it carries out basic training such as the language course (illustrated) and continuation training for the 1,200 soldiers who currently serve with some 29 units and sub-units of the Hong Kong Garrison. In 1991 a detachment served in Cyprus as part of BRITCON within UNFICYP.

Below: A squad of the Hong Kong Military Service Corps formed up ready to march to the ranges on Stonecutters Island for musketry instruction. Whatever the role of the soldier within the Army, all receive basic infantry training of drill and musketry, to instil discipline and to ensure that point defence can be undertaken in the event of an attack.

Above, centre right and bottom right: Following the introduction of the SA80 and the cost of the SUSAT sight, a variant is issued to some units which does not have the sight fitted. Instead it has the traditional iron sights. Due to the design of the SA80 this has resulted in the rear sight being raised to such a degree that it has been incorporated into a handle. A basic training version of the SA80 known as the Ensign training rifle is intended for use by the Army Cadets. The Ensign has a self-loading single-shot mechanism to replace the gas operated mechanism and without the grenade launching attachment. A further variant is designed to fire the .22 ammunition. Here soldiers of the HKMSC undergo their rifle training course. The shipping and the buildings in the background illustrate the problem of safety for the firing of live weapons in Hong Kong.

Above: In line with most regiments, the HKMSC has its own highly professional band. The Military bands are an appealing way of catching the ear and eye of the general public. Such is the popularity of the HKMSC band that in addition to their parades and public concerts they get numerous bookings for private functions around Hong Kong.

Left: 660 Squadron is based at Sek Kong with its Westland Scout AH.1. It has a detached Flight in Brunei in support of the Gurkha Battalion based there. The Scout is used as a reconnaissance platform as well as a means of communication. This Scout is on approach to the Headquarters British Forces Hong Kong aboard HMS *Tamar*.

Norway

Each year a number of reinforcement exercises are held in Norway. The United Kingdom Mobile Force (UKMF) consisting of 1 Infantry Brigade plus a Logistic Support Group is dedicated to the reinforcement of the Baltic Approaches. In addition the NATO Allied Command Europe (ACE) Mobile Force is maintained in readiness to support either the northern or southern flanks. To this force the British Army provides 2,300 men comprising an infantry battalion, reconnaissance, artillery, helicopter, signals and logistics units. In addition, the army provides a 105mm Light Gun regiment and two engineer squadrons to the UK/Netherlands Amphibious Force for deployment to the Northern Flank.

Right: The exercises held in Norway are based on the rapid reinforcement of the Norwegian Armed Forces. Being a quick reaction force, the UKLF is equipped with the lighter AFVs such as the Scimitar (illustrated) which is able to cross snow relatively easily. The role of the UKLF is to move rapidly into position as a deterrent in time of tension, and to act as a holding force until further reinforcements arrive.

Opposite page, top: Camouflage is arguably more necessary in an Arctic environment than in any other because of the unrelenting white scenery. Most Army equipment is painted black and green to conform with a normal European terrain. During Arctic exercises a number of vehicles and helicopters receive varying amounts of white markings, and different trials have been conducted over the years to evaluate the effect. No doubt in an emergency all equipment and vehicles would receive an appropriate finish as did those that were shipped out to the Gulf. For the UKLF, though, there might be insufficient time to do this. Whatever the situation, soldiers will be trying their best to disguise vehicles and stores and one of the most effective means is camouflage netting.

Opposite page, bottom: Winter camouflage for the troops is provided by a white lightweight over suit which includes a helmet cover. Camouflage has also been applied to the SA80 in an attempt to break up its shape. This SA80 is being used without the SUSAT sight.

Right: In northern Norway the environment is typically arctic and the troops need to be taught to ski. Once mastered, it enables country to be crossed rapidly. Supplies can be carried on small sleighs.

Below: The plan is always the first thing to go wrong, so good planning bears this in mind. When a vehicle breaks down the REME FV106 Samson will be dispatched. It is based on the Spartan's basic structure with various additions including a powerful winch that can pull 12 tonnes – three tonnes more than its own weight. When pulling such weights a pair of large spades is deployed to anchor the vehicle. A range of tools can be carried although internal space is limited because of the winch. The Spartan is manned by a crew of three.

Above: Members of the Royal Wessex Yeomanry guard the exercise HQ which is situated in their local Trowbridge TA centre. While the TA are involved in a number of weekend 'local' exercises mounted by individual units, and in the annual camp which can be abroad, occasionally larger exercises are carried out to practise co-ordinated training.

Exercise 'Drake's Drum' was one such exercise which combined the deployment of 1,200 TA personnel including the Home Service Force plus 1,100 Reservists. In addition 2,100 Regulars took part, mainly to provide the 'enemy' and umpire organizations.

Left: The purpose of Exercise 'Drake's Drum' was so that the TA and HSF could practise their role of defending and guarding important installations which might be targets for espionage, subversion or sabotage by enemy forces in a time of tension. To give realism to the exercise RAF Hercules dropped enemy intruders by parachute. Others dressed as civilians were less obvious which meant that all visitors to establishments had to be thoroughly checked.

Territorial Army

The Territorial Army is a vital part of today's British Army, its role being to boost the strength of the Regular Army in an emergency, which it has been doing since it was formed in 1920. It comprises a large number of regional units of civilians from all walks of life, to make up approximately one-third of the strength of the British Army. The range of roles of the TA units is as varied as those of the Regular Army because each is attached to a Regular regiment or corps.

The TA comprises part-time volunteers plus the Individual Reserve who are ex-Regular servicemen and are required to remain on the reserve for some time once they have left the Army. While useful, it is not mandatory for TA volunteers to have had a military background, but the standards for joining are the same as those for joining the Regulars. The commitment for those accepted is to 'sign on' for a three-year period during which they must complete a 15-day camp and sixteen separate training days each year. Opportunities available are varied.

While some exercises can be arduous, they may be conducted overseas in Germany, Cyprus, Canada or Belize, and on full rates of pay and allowances. The recent Gulf War saw the mobilization of a number of the TA units, for the first time since the Suez crisis. A total of 1,620 Reservists were deployed to the Gulf for all three services, and a number of others replaced those Regular personnel who had already been posted to the Gulf. Most of the TA medical units were flown out to the Gulf as were a number of other specialist units.

The 1981 Defence Review detailed an eight-year plan to expand the TA from 74,000 to 86,000 and to create a 5,000-strong Home Service Force (HSF) of former TA soldiers. Despite a recruitment drive this was never achieved and by 1990 the TA was 15,000 below its target strength of 91,000. With the Options for Change this is planned to drop to between 60,000 and 65,000.

Right: It is just as important that the TA and reservists train against the threat of an NBC attack as it is for the Regular Army. Here members of the TA in full NBC clothing guard the South West District Headquarters at Bulford.

Left: TA soldiers are trained in NBC conditions to get them accustomed to working in the clothing. Having been flown in by helicopter, the soldiers have to check live Milan missiles before being moved to a firing point to fire them. Exertion in NBC clothing can cause problems, and the conditions are a severe test of a soldier, especially those from the TA.

Below: Members of the Milan Platoon of 1st Battalion, The Wessex Regiment based in Gloucester, pose for a photograph at their Headquarters before travelling to a firing camp.

Right: At Otterburn training ground equipment is set up and the safety rules implemented. It is now that the last twelve months' training will be tested. At the far end of the range a target board moves from left to right. At the firing point each of the missile operators is allocated a missile and will go through the sequence of running up to the firing point with the missile, breathlessly loading, aiming, firing and flying the missile to the target. Those who hit the target have qualified. For those that didn't there is another twelve months of training before the next live firing opportunity.

Right: For the Air Defence Regiments the training is similar although they are fortunate enough to get a warm-up. To keep Javelin training costs down the Army have purchased the Dart. This is a dummy missile which is loaded and fired in exactly the same way as Javelin, but the missile is totally inert and once blown out of the launcher will fall to the ground some 40–50 metres from the launch point.

Dart gives the trainee firer an introduction to a live missile launch which he cannot experience during his training in the simulator. The next stage for this soldier from 102 (Ulster and Scottish) Air Defence Regiment (V) is to fire his first live Javelin, but the initial blast will not now cause him the same distraction.

Right: The Shorts Skeet Mk 2 is used on ranges to give a realistic quick-reaction aerial target system for use with close-range weapons such as the Javelin. It has a wing span of 2.72 metres, is launched by a self-contained, pneumatically operated launcher and is controlled in flight by radio command at ranges of up to 5 kilometres. It can fly at up to 150 knots, has an endurance of 75 minutes and is fitted with sixteen smoke flares for a smoke-enhanced target. The accuracy of missiles fired at Skeet are measured by a miss-distance indicator.

Left: Once the Skeet is off down range the tension tightens as the operator pushes the aiming unit on to the missile canister. He lifts the Javelin to his shoulder, his instructor checks that he is ready and the Skeet turns in. A smoke flare is ignited on the Skeet which is now about four to five kilometres out. Once it has been spotted the operator tracks it in his viewfinder. When steady he advises the instructor who gives the clear to fire. The operator presses the fire button and there is a pop as the plastic bung blows out, followed shortly after by a blast and the missile emerges and within a second or so is at Mach 2.

Left: By keeping the target on the aiming mark the Javelin missile will automatically fly to the target using the SACLOS (Semi-Automatic Command to Line Of Sight) guidance system. As it gets closer there is a flash and the next thing is that the Skeet can be seen tumbling from the sky until it deploys a parachute.

The Skeet comprises nine modules, each of which can be replaced if damaged. At the end of its flight the Skeet can be landed conventionally on its skid or recovered by parachute on command. The parachute will also automatically deploy in the event of a command link failure, such as here, when it has been hit. A miss indicator is fitted to the Skeet because, it being small the missile might fly close enough without actually hitting to have been considered a hit on a full-sized aircraft.

Left: A patrol is alarmed and drop to the ground in an all points defensive posture. The nearest soldier is equipped with the 7.62mm SLR fitted with the SUIT (Sight Unit Infantry Trilux) while the soldier behind him has the GPMG.

Right: The 7.62mm SLR or L1A1 as designated in the Army identifying system is being superseded by the SA80. This gun fires the 5.56mm ammunition which being lighter allows the soldier to carry more rounds for the equivalent amount of weight. The SLR has been a tough, well-used and dependable rifle. Despite its being longer than the SA80 (1.143m compared to .785m) and slightly heavier (5.074kg compared to 4.86kg) it has been popular with the troops.

Right: Soldiers firing the 7.62mm SLR and GPMG at pop-up targets on the Walcop ranges. The SLR has a firing rate of 40 rounds per minute compared with the GPMGs either of 100 rpm or 625/750 in the sustained fire mode. The SLR has a range of 600m while the GPMG is 800m in the light role which increases to 1,800m in the sustained fire mode.

Right: Often called the Stirling, the L2A3 is a 9mm submachine-gun mainly used by engineers, artillery and second-line troops. The soldier seen here is progressing along a live firing range where pop-up targets present themselves; his instructor marks his reaction and accuracy.

Top left and left: An instructor demonstrates the correct way to remove the pin from and throw an anti-personnel L2 HE Hand-Grenade to his group before they are taken into the pit to throw their first grenades.

Above, right and far right: A line-up of Fox from A Squadron, The Royal Wiltshire Yeomanry, at the firing point for a practice firing camp at Walcop. The Fox is fitted with the Rarden turret which has the 30mm plus a 7.62 machine-gun. It can take 99 rounds of the 30mm ammunition plus 2,600 rounds of 7.62mm.

In the last photograph the Fox can be seen firing its GPMG at a low target.

IOFD93

Left: On completing the firing camp all weapons are stripped and cleaned. Among the weapons here are the Stirling L2A3 Machine-Gun, the GPMG, L4A4 'Bren Gun' and the SLR.

Left: The FV105 Sultan has a raised box hull to give sufficient capacity for the crew and the map boards. It is unlikely that sufficient room is available to accommodate any of the additional officers for briefings and so a penthouse can be erected over the back to give some protection from the elements.

Left: Soldiers from the Royal Wiltshire Yeomanry camouflage their Fox on the edge of woodland to enable them discreetly to observe enemy movements. There is one Regular armoured reconnaissance regiment equipped with the CVR(W) Fox plus the two TA regiments that will be reinforcing BAOR – the Royal Yeomanry and the Queen's Own Yeomanry.

Right: Soldiers from the Royal Wiltshire Yeomanry on a break from their exercise prepare some 'scoff' and a brew. Compo ration packs are issued prior to the exercise and when required.

Below: A swiftly moving FV103 Spartan armoured personnel carrier, powered by its Jaguar J60 which can accelerate it to more than 80km/h on roads. It is manned by a crew of three: commander, driver and machine-gunner, and can carry four soldiers with their equipment.

Above: Four troops await the approaching Scout helicopter from 666 Squadron for the heli lift to their next position. The Scout can carry four troops in addition to its crew of two although one of the crew can be dispensed with to give extra space. In the past the Scout also provided an ATGW capability but this role is now carried out by the Lynx.

Left: On 1 April 1986, 666 Squadron was reformed as an independent TA unit. Based at Netheravon, it is part of 7 Regiment and flies the Westland Scout AH.1 in the utility role. The Scout has proved itself to be an extremely rugged helicopter over the years and is ideally suited for TA use.